POSITION OF T

Welcome to POSITION OF THE WEEK – the book that puts the fun back into love-making!

You see, a lot of people don't realise that there's a gloriously funny side to making love. It's an activity which should very often make you *laugh* together – as well as making the two of you feel happy and romantic.

What we offer you is this: *a different love-making position for every week of the year*. And if you can manage them *ALL* in the course of a twelvemonth, then I must say you'll have done incredibly well. Good luck.

**Also by the same author,
and available from NEL:**

It's a Doc's Life
The Book of Love
How To Improve Your Sex Life
The Home Doctor
The Delvin Report

About the author

Dr David Delvin was born in Dublin and Glasgow (it
was a rather complicated delivery). Contrary to what
many people believe, he really IS a doctor – and an
elected member of the General Medical Council.

He is a veteran of over 700 TV programmes,
including *Mastermind* (during which his fellow doctors suggested that one of his specialist subjects
should be 'Trouble Down Below'). He is married to
the TV presenter Christine Webber.

In *The Observer* magazine Dr David Delvin was
selected as the media medic's expert by the experts'
expert, Dr Mike Smith, who said "David Delvin . . .
[has] the knack of making medicine not only com-
prehensible to lay people, but non-threatening as
well."

Position of the week

DR DAVID DELVIN

With illustrations by David Arrowsmith

NEW ENGLISH LIBRARY
Hodder and Stoughton

First published in Great Britain in
1991 by New English Library
Paperbacks Ltd.

*A New English Library paperback
original*

British Library C.I.P.

Delvin David
  Position of the week.
  I. Title
613.9

  ISBN 0-450-55452-X

Printed and bound in Great Britain
for Hodder and Stoughton Paper-
backs, a division of Hodder and
Stoughton Ltd., Mill Road, Dunton
Green, Sevenoaks, Kent TN13
2YA. (Editorial Office: 47 Bedford
Square, London WC1B 3DP) by
Clays Ltd., St Ives plc. Typeset by
Rowland Phototypesetting Ltd.,
Bury St Edmunds, Suffolk.

"To-morrow to fresh woods, and postures new."
—after Milton (*Lycidas*)

ACKNOWLEDGMENTS

My grateful thanks to:

CHRISTINE WEBBER (my wife) for helping to bring out the Joycean nuances of the subtext;
DAVID ARROWSMITH (the artist) for not being too shocked at what he had to draw;
DOUGLAS WEBBER (my father-in-law) for the use of his bus pass at a critical moment.

APPEAL

The photographs on which these fifty-two positions are based were unfortunately lost during a matinée of *The Phantom of the Opera* (having been placed under a seat in the stalls for safe-keeping).

So if YOU attended a recent performance at Her Majesty's Theatre and found a plain brown envelope containing Polaroids of a lady and gent (in tracksuits, of course) demonstrating various unusual contortions, could you please return them to me, c/o Hodder & Stoughton?

The usual discreet reward will be paid.

CONTENTS

INTRODUCTION

Welcome to *Position of the Week* – the book that puts the fun back into love-making!

You see, a lot of people don't realise that there's a gloriously funny side to making love. It's an activity which should very often make you *laugh* together – as well as making the two of you feel happy and romantic.

Indeed, there are very few things which are as hilariously dotty as the sight of two human beings attempting to get into some exotic position, with the *Kama Sutra* in one hand and *Gray's Anatomy* in the other!

Actually, this book is a bit different from both the *Kama Sutra* and Dr Gray's anatomical masterpiece – because what it mainly aims to do is to help you both have FUN.

What we offer you is this: *a different love-making position for every week of the year*. And if you can manage them ALL in the course of a twelvemonth, then I must say you'll have done incredibly well.

By the way, some readers of my columns in women's magazines have in the past got slightly the wrong idea about these exotic positions. Let me make it quite clear that you DON'T have to "go all the way" in them. In other words, you don't have to *stay* in them till you reach a climax!

No: the general idea is that you just sort of "dip into" a position for a few minutes or so. If you both like it a lot, then by all means go on with it till things reach their natural conclusion. But it may well be that, after a few dozen sensuous thrusts in position number twenty-three or thirty-seven or forty-one, you'll feel like reverting to whatever posture is usually the most comfortable and romantic for you both. And jolly good luck to you.

Incidentally, you may well ask: why *have* all these different sex positions? What's the justification for them? Well, I can think of *four* justifications:

1. Quite a few people with arthritis and rheumatism (seriously!) do find it difficult to make love in the regular way which they've used in the past. Trying a different posture often makes life a great deal easier for them. (That also applies to some handicapped people.)

2. During pregnancy, many women find that sex in positions such as the "Missionary" is very difficult and uncomfortable; a change (especially a change to "woman-superior" positions) makes everything OK again.

3. In many ordinary love-making positions (such as the "Missionary"), it's *extremely* difficult for the man to stimulate the woman's clitoris with his hand. Yet most women like to have their clitorises stroked or rubbed during intercourse!

Indeed, latest research shows that many ladies can't reach a climax *unless* they're receiving both vaginal AND clitoral stimulation at the same time.

So, there's obviously a great deal to be said for positions in which the gent can actually manage to reach his lady's clitoris. This is such an important point that throughout the book we've given each position a special "Clitoris Rating", ranging from *zero* up to *C C C*!

4. If a loving couple try out various sex positions together, it does "relieve the monogamy" – in other words, it helps keep that essential spice and freshness in a relationship – and so (with luck) helps keep the couple *faithful* to each other.

And, dear Heaven, fidelity is what we desperately need these days! In the "Nervous 1990s" of the Aids era, it's vital that – instead of continuing to ride on the "sexual roundabout" of the

60s, 70s and 80s – we now try to stick to one partner, and one only.

Try all of the positions in this volume, and I'm *sure* you'll stick to the same partner. Probably permanently. (Information on how to contact a good osteopath is printed on the last page of the book.)

POSITION NUMBER ONE: CLITORIS RATING: C C (if he's left-handed)

The Bergerac

We begin the first week of the New Year with the very comfortable and romantic position known in France as "Le Bergerac".

It's good for ladies who are pregnant or who have artificial or arthritic hips (this is not a joke), but it's also jolly nice for almost *anybody*.

What you do is this. You, ma'am, should lie on your back – just like the intrepid lady shown in the picture. Your husband (at least, I HOPE he's your husband) should then lie next to you on your left. As you can see, he's lying on his right side.

Now *madame*, please lift your left foot in the air in an obliging fashion – in Scotland at the New Year, this is known as "first footing" – so that your bloke can slide his left leg under YOUR left leg, but on top of your right thigh.

(Got it so far? There'll be an exam paper at the end, remember . . .)

Then your man gently kisses you; you guide him in with your free right hand – and away you go.

Incidentally, you may well wonder why our first position is known as "Bergerac".

Some folk say that it's named after Police-Sergeant Bergerac, the hero of the popular BBC-TV detective series set in fairly romantic Jersey.

Others claim that it's something to do with the sun-filled and agreeable *vin de Bergerac* – a very drinkable *plonkette*, available in both red and white, which originates from the south slopes of the Dordogne valley.

Still others maintain that the Bergerac position was the one which was most favoured by the great French swordsman Cyrano de Bergerac, presumably because it gave him plenty of room for his nose (not to mention his *panache*).

All wrong, I'm afraid. Actually, I picked the name out of a list of French Rugby teams. (Caution: not all of the position titles in this book are quite what they seem . . .)

POSITION NUMBER TWO:
CLITORIS RATING: C C C

The Lyons

No, the Lyons position, which we show here, is nothing to do with the well-known British tea-rooms of the same name – once famous for their nice waitresses with black dresses and starched aprons.

In fact, the honest truth is that this exotic posture is called after the central French city of Lyon (which *les français*, somewhat perversely, spell without an "s").

Why is it so named? Well, according to the US sex guru Dr Alex Comfort, there once used to be a somewhat badly sprung stagecoach which travelled between Lyon and Paris. The occupants of this exceedingly bumpy vehicle realised that it produced a sensation not unlike that experienced by the oscillating lady in our picture!

Anyway, the position is certainly much more fun than riding in some jolting old stagecoach – and you DON'T need a coach to do it on: just a bed or a couch or a floor. Many women like the Lyons position because of the fact that it doesn't put any weight on their tummies – and also because it does give a quite exquisite degree of penetration. Many ladies say that they experience a great sense of abandonment – and sheer fun.

On a practical note, the position does also give a chap a decent chance of stimulating his lady-love's *cli-cli*: hence its high "Clitoris Rating" (see above). That factor does greatly increase the chance that the woman will reach a climax.

As you can probably see from our drawing, getting into this posture is pretty easy – though STAYING in it may be a teeny bit more tricky, ma'am, as your chap grows steadily more enthusiastic!

So to begin making love in the Lyons position, all that's necessary is for the bloke to lie down on some fairly firm surface. Once he has attained an erection, and once the lady is sure that she is reasonably well lubricated, he simply invites her to climb aboard. In order that things should be as comfortable as possible for her, it's important that *she* does the "guiding in" of his organ.

Her feet should be about level with his ears, and he should kick off by holding her bottom (as shown) so that he can keep her fairly steadily balanced while he bounces her up and down.

One word of warning, ma'am: do take care NOT to fall off your gent suddenly, since this could cause him a nasty injury. (I am *not* joking.)

8

POSITION NUMBER THREE:
CLITORIS RATING: NIL

The Missionary

This is, of course, the most common way of making love. It's pleasant and comfortable and romantic, and – very important – the couple can actually TALK to each other while they're doing it.

Also, the Missionary position gives you the opportunity to kiss each other on the lips, which is very important for a lot of couples (not all, though: some women have a real aversion to being kissed while they have sex; that clearly does *not* apply to the lady missionary in our picture).

Disadvantages? The position's usually rather uncomfortable for a woman who's any degree advanced in pregnancy. And it does make it VERY difficult for the chap to stimulate the lady's clitoris with his fingertips.

Indeed, in this position many women find that it's easier to stimulate their clitorises *themselves* – rather than have the bloke try and bend his hand round agonisingly backwards in order to do it. Don't be shocked at that: my national sex surveys show that the majority of wives don't mind resorting to this "DIY" ruse in order to reach orgasm.

Now why on earth is this called the "missionary position"? Most sex books make the claim that it's because missionaries in tropical lands taught their flocks that this was the only acceptable way to make love – and that all others were "rude".

I don't know of the slightest real evidence for that theory, and all the missionaries I've ever met have been far too sensible to go round propagating such nonsense.

However, I'm afraid that this position is now stuck forever with the title "Missionary" – and all over the world, there are young men who fantasize about beautiful lady missionaries, lying back in the jungle and raising their splendid lily-white thighs towards the tropical sun . . .

Furthermore, a medical colleague of mine from the South Seas tells me that he once heard of a cantankerous and repressive old Scots clergyman who went out to the islands and told the natives that they must only have intercourse "in the regular way". They promptly ate him.

Six months later, an easy-going French missionary turned up at the same group of islands, established a small Catholic church, and told the islanders that they could make love any way they wanted (a popular ruling, that).

One day he asked his flock to tell him what they'd done with the Scots minister, and they replied to the effect that they had boiled him up in the pot with some coconuts and bananas.

"That was very, very wrong," exclaimed the shocked priest.

"Really?" responded the surprised cannibal chief.

"Oh yes, *mon fils*," admonished the Frenchman. "You should 'ave sautéed 'im lightly with *fines herbes* and a leetle white sauce . . ."

POSITION NUMBER FOUR:
CLITORIS RATING: NIL

The Narbonne

The Narbonne position is a good one for lovers who want to try something that is comfortable and romantic, but quite exotic too. As you can see from this week's drawing, the lady sits on the edge of a low couch or bed, with her legs raised.

Then the chap kneels on the floor in front of her and gently enters her – following which, she can draw him in quite deeply if she wants to, by crossing her legs and pulling him towards her with her thighs.

A good position, but, like the "Missionary", it offers virtually no access by the male hand to the clitoris – unless the gent happens to be something of an amateur contortionist.

The "Narbonne" is of course named after Violette de Narbonne, the legendary nineteenth century Paris courtesan who always employed it, because it gave her what she called "*la meilleure pénétration*".

Her use of this position made her famous, and men throughout France were desperate to buy her favours – for which she charged 1,000 gold francs a night.

Indeed, the officer-cadets at the military academy of St Cyr were so entranced by stories of her and of her amazing new position that (although they were very poor) they clubbed together to raise the 1,000 francs. And they then drew lots to see who would be lucky enough to have the privilege of sleeping with her.

The winner was the youngest cadet, who'd only been able to contribute a meagre 10 centimes to the kitty.

But he duly went along to see Mlle de Narbonne, gave her the bag of money, and spent an extremely passionate night with her – mostly in the Narbonne position.

In the morning, the young man awoke – with *very* sore kneecaps – and told the beautiful courtesan the story of how the officer-cadets had collected the 1,000 gold francs.

And *la Narbonne* was so deeply moved by his tale that she wiped away a tear, reached across the bed, picked up the money bag – and gave him back his 10 centimes.

POSITION NUMBER FIVE:
CLITORIS RATING: NIL

The Vienna

This position was invented by Johann Strauss the Elder and Fraulein Mitzi von Schnitzel at the Congress of Vienna in 1814 – and recent musicological research has strongly suggested that it was eventually responsible for the birth of Johann Strauss the Younger in 1825. (Old Johann was never one to rush his *tempi*.)

Ladies: the "Vienna" is achieved by lying flat on top of your man – and then turning yourself through 90° so that your body is at right-angles to his.

To be utterly frank (and we're nothing if not frank in this book), you, ma'am, should then receive pleasantly unusual sensations from the pressure of his erect organ against the SIDE wall of your vagina.

What else can one say about this romantic posture, so redolent of the *gemütlichkeit* of the era of the Hapsburg emperors? (You can practically hear *The Blue Danube* as you do it!)

Well, it doesn't give much opportunity for witty conversation, that's for sure. On the other hand, recent investigation does strongly suggest that the Vienna position did enable the elder Johann to keep his hand in (musically speaking, of course) by tapping out all his famous Viennese waltz rhythms on his lady-love's bottom while they made love.

And here we see him – happily running his gifted fingers up

and down Fraulein von Schnitzel's amazing Austrian arpeggio . . .

POSITION NUMBER SIX:
CLITORIS RATING: C C C

The Earthquake

The "Earthquake" position is said to have been used for the first time by a lusty young couple who were making love in San Francisco on the night of 18 April 1906.

Nancy O'Hara was one of the quite substantial minority of girls who don't actually want to be kissed *on the lips* during love-making.

So her handsome and considerate swain, gallant young Chauncey McPeake, invented this position for her.

If you want to try out Chauncey's invention, dear readers, what you do is this. The lady must kneel *upright*. The gent must kneel down behind her, also erect (he hopes . . .). His knees have to be between hers.

Next, he gently inserts himself into her vagina from behind – and the operative word, gentlemen, is "gently"! Do NOT ram yourself forward in haste, or you may give your missus a most uncomfortable prod – and in a most uncomfortable place, too.

As far as *you* are concerned, ma'am, you should use your hand (just as fair young Nancy did, so long ago) to help him pop it in. And – very important – you will need to *keep* your hand in front of your vulva during most of intercourse, in order to stop him from slipping out.

This, please note, is one of those excellent "Clitoris Rating" positions in which the man – or, indeed, the lady herself – can

very easily stimulate the clitoral area during intercourse, thus greatly increasing the chances of an orgasm.

Yes, young Chauncey's clitoral stimulation of the beauteous Nancy was so effective back in 1906 that she readily achieved a climax which measured 9.3 on the Richter scale. On recovering, she was the first-ever person to utter the immortal words, "Did the earth move for you too?"

NOTE: many *literati* quite wrongly attribute the first use of that phrase to Ernest Hemingway in *For Whom The Bell Tolls* (1940; chapter 13).

In fact, Hemingway had overheard the expression in 1907 when he attended Chauncey and Nancy's wedding – as a pageboy. He was understandably not keen to admit this.

So much for the *literati* (or, indeed, the *cliterati*).

POSITION NUMBER SEVEN:
CLITORIS RATING: C C C

The Chalet

And now, the Chalet position: invented, of course, by a Swiss couple (who were, as you can see, on their honeymoon in Bognor Regis at the time). I always feel that the great thing about it is that it's so very *comfortable*.

This sense of comfort and reassurance makes it just the thing for couples who're just beginning their relationship, or who are perhaps a little nervous about sex. I would recommend it if a couple have some minor sexual difficulty – f'rinstance, if the bloke's a little worried about his potency, or if the lady's tummy is a bit tender for some reason.

And the Chalet position is particularly useful in pregnancy, because – as you can see – there's absolutely no weight on the woman's tum.

Also, it's really one of the easiest and most natural of sex positions. All that the lass has to do is to lie flat on her back, with her knees raised. And all the lad has to do is to lie alongside her (on his side), and then curl his thighs up under her bottom. He may then need the assistance of her hand to get him gently into her vagina – following which, everything should be delightfully straightforward and agreeable.

A good point about the Chalet position is that there's ample room for him to caress her breasts and clitoris with his left hand. (If you're *right*-handed, sir, you may prefer to lie on the other side of the lady.)

Incidentally, when I first described this position in the pages of that well-known medical journal *SHE*, I had a complaint from one of Britain's most respected book reviewers, Ms Val Hennessey. She sent a message *via* my Editor to say that the Chalet posture was "impossible"!

Well, I do hope you've got it right by now, Val. I'm sorry I can't come round and show you, but I'm afraid I don't make house calls.

POSITION NUMBER EIGHT: CLITORIS RATING: C C

The Florentine

I honestly don't know why sex textbooks refer to this as "the Florentine position". In my Larousse dictionary, there are two definitions of the word "Florentine", one of which is:

"On a bed of stewed spinach; covered with Mornay sauce; then sprinkled with grated cheese."

Well, you'll be glad to know that this week's position definitely *doesn't* involve doing anything on a bed of stewed spinach!

The other definition is, of course, "pertaining to Florence" (no, *not* the one on the Magic Roundabout).

So, I can only presume that in the fabled city of the Ponte Vecchio, some intrepid couple like Dante and Beatrice invented this quite spectacular *postura*. I expect that was the occasion which Dante referred to in his famous line "*E quinde uscimmo, a riveder le stelle*" ("Thus we came, and saw the stars once more").

Anyway, it's a jolly good *postura* – and an excellent feature of it is the fact that it's a great help to the many men who have a slight uncertainty about their *erezione*.

What basically happens is that the *signore* lies flat upon his *dorso*, with his *ginocchi* spread wide, as you can see.

The *signora* then mounts him – but throughout the entire *azione*, she keeps her *mano* on his *pene*. (If you want some

romantic background music for this, a suitable piece would be *La ci darem la mano . . .*)

Actually, the hand position gives the *signore* really superb sensations, as well as helping him to maintain his stiffness, should he have any moments of nervousness. I'm told that the sensation is nice for the *signora* too!

A slightly different view of the Florentine position is given by world sexpert Dr Alex Comfort. He says that the main point of the position is that the lady should pull the gentleman's penile skin (including his foreskin, if he has one) as far DOWN-WARDS as possible, so that it's stretched as tightly as possible over his organ, right up to the moment of climax.

Sounds Dante to me . . .

POSITION NUMBER NINE: CLITORIS RATING: C

Stade Français

Now, have you been making love in a more or less horizontal position for years?

Do you need something new, in order to make sex more varied for the two of you?

Well, Stade Français could be the answer! Pay no attention to the fact that "standing sex" has had a bit of a bad press in recent years – mainly because it tends to be used for illicit passion by young couples who have no bedroom to go to.

But it can be very pleasant if you're both in the mood, and a lot of loving couples do like the sheer abandoned "naughtiness" of it all.

Some use it while fantasising that they're making love behind the bike-sheds (NOT something that I'd ever recommend you to try in real life; for one thing, it could be far too chilly).

Since men are usually a bit taller than their female partners, it's easier if the man can arrange things so that he stands just a little lower than his lady. If you don't do this, it can all be a bit of a strain on the legs – and you'll probably find out why this position is often referred to as "the dreaded knee-trembler"!

So, in this "staircase" version (overleaf) of the Stade Français position, *monsieur* is standing one step below *madame* on their modest little Paris *escalier*.

Indeed, life may be more comfortable for them if – as in our picture – she raises one foot and puts it a bit higher up the staircase. That will improve the access to her *cli-cli*, which would otherwise be quite difficult in this position.

Incidentally, if the chap is SHORTER than his lady, there's no need at all for him to stand on a lower step. Indeed, if he's very short, it may be easier for them if he puts his feet on a step ABOVE the one she's standing on. Napoleon frequently did this with Josephine; hence his famous dictum: "There is only one step from the sublime to the ridiculous."

FOOTNOTE: There is still a persistent myth to the effect that you "can't get pregnant" in this position. You can.

POSITION NUMBER TEN:
CLITORIS RATING: C C C *

The Spoons

So called because you and your partner are tucked up snugly together like two spoons in a drawer.

As you can doubtless see, this is a jolly nice, comfortable position, which is *particularly* useful in pregnancy, because it doesn't put even the slightest weight on the lady's lower abdomen.

It's also exceptionally helpful for the quite HUGE number of women who can't reach orgasm during intercourse, but would like to do so.

Why? Because the bloke can easily reach round with his hand – just as the chap in the picture is doing – and stimulate his loved one's clitoris with his fingertips. (That, of course, is the reason for this position's exceptional "rosette" in the Clitoris Ratings.)

I first recommended the Spoons position in a women's magazine many years ago, stressing that it was a great help for women who wanted to climax during intercourse. You may find this hard to believe, but in those days – the early 1970s – the opposition to "rear-entry" positions was still so great that I received quite a lot of abusive mail!

In particular, the magazine's Agony Auntie, who was the famous romantic novelist Miss Denise Robins, wrote me an indignant letter in which she said that "no decent girl would

allow herself to be penetrated from the rear". She felt that such positions were "unromantic and degrading".

However, I'm glad to say that before she died, Denise and I became fast friends – and I was eventually able to convince her that there are often good reasons why a couple would want to make love in this warm, cuddly position.

Nonetheless, I don't think that she ever decided to include the Spoons position in even the most *abandoned* of her later romantic novels!

To get into the position, all you need do is cuddle up together as shown in the picture. If your man is right-handed, ma'am, you may find it better if you both lie on your LEFT sides. Once you're well lubricated, ease him in gently – and away you go . . . Have a nice time.

POSITION NUMBER ELEVEN:
CLITORIS RATING: C

The Bristol

Now you've heard the expression "All shipshape and Bristol fashion". Well, this IS the Bristol fashion – practised by generations of Bristolian ladies and their seafaring lovers.

What you do is to start off as though you were getting into the Lyons position (please see Week Two). In other words, the lady sits up on top of her man, having slipped his erect penis inside her. Having achieved this, she should spend a minute or two just gently *swaying* from side to side, imagining that she's the mast of a sailing ship, caught in the trade winds of love . . .

Now you'll note that her feet are kept very close to her body – resting on her bloke's chest, in fact. Ladies who are really skilled exponents of the Bristolian position can even tickle their lover's nipples with their toes!

Next comes the really unusual thing about the Bristol-fashion posture. Helped by the gent, the gallant lass actually turns herself through 360°. (This is known in nautical terms as "boxing the compass".)

If you're not clear what I mean, ma'am, just follow the direction of the arrows in the picture. Begin by turning your entire body through 90°, so that you're sideways on your man, with your feet on the bed beside him.

Now continue the turn through a further 90°, so that you're facing AWAY from him. (Your feet will now be somewhere near his knees.)

Carry on turning, all the way round, until you're facing him again. (Phew!) This unique circular manoeuvre should give both of you some very jolly sensations – for the effect of it is that his erect organ will actually turn a complete circle inside your vagina as you sweep round. (Indeed, this is the only sexual position which can quite genuinely be described as "a screw".)

As for *you*, sir, the most important thing you have to remember is that the Bristol position is inherently an unsteady one – so it's essential that you take the responsibility for making sure that your "shipmate" doesn't fall off you!

So in order to keep the female mate "steady as she goes", it's usual for the Jolly Jack Tar down below to take a firm grip of her breasts.

Indeed, in the most exotic refinement of this position, the sailor gently massages his lady-love's bosom throughout the entire operation, using a traditional maritime aphrodisiac application. It's called "Bristol Cream".

POSITION NUMBER TWELVE:
CLITORIS RATING: C C C

Free As Air

If I can tell you the honest truth for once (instead of a load of old flannel), this position was *genuinely* given the name "Free As Air" by a lady who helped to invent it – and who found that it produced a delightfully liberated sensation of floating along on a cloud.

She says: "The position seems to me to be the only one in which a woman feels totally *independent*. When I make love like this, I have a sensation of being completely unshackled, mainly because there's absolutely no weight on me at all. It's as if I'm flying along gently."

However, the "flying" sensation isn't *quite* so gentle (points out the lady) as the man approaches his climax. She adds: "As he makes his final thrusts, you feel as if you're being catapulted up towards the sky. And if you happen to reach orgasm yourself at that moment, it's absolute bliss . . ."

In fact, this position is one which is particularly likely to help women reach orgasm, and I'd strongly recommend it for anyone who's having difficulty in that direction. I'll tell you why in a moment.

But first, a brief explanation of how you actually get into the (fairly complex) "Free As Air" position – because if you don't get it right, it'll be uncomfortable and unsatisfying.

So – after the usual agreeable foreplay has been completed

(so that the woman's love juices are really flowing), the man should lie flat on his back on the bed. The lady should then sit on him – facing away from him – and gently ease his organ inside with her hand.

Next, she leans right back so that her face nestles alongside his. In order to keep her balance, she may need to hang on to his arm, as we've shown. And she may well have to put one hand in front of her vulva in order to keep her man from popping out.

All set? Then let the gentleman start thrusting gently – and you, ma'am, will find yourself flying along . . .

Now the reasons *why* so many women find "Free As Air" to be a position that helps them reach orgasm:

First, it's VERY easy for the chap to reach round and give her clitoris really intensive stimulation.

Second, the lady has complete freedom to "take charge" by rubbing her own clitoris if she wants to. That's probably why this position is so popular with independent-minded career ladies who like to take things into their own hands (if you'll forgive the phrase).

Third, the woman can move her limbs to whatever position she wants them in, *without any constraints being put on her by the man*. Few sexual postures are as totally untrammelled for the woman as this one is! Again, this is a point which appeals to the free-spirited, independent woman who likes to be boss of her own destiny.

POSITION NUMBER THIRTEEN:
CLITORIS RATING: C

The Seville

Well now, the Seville position was of course the one used by Carmen in her famous encounter with the handsome *torero* – NOT "toreador", please – called Escamillo. (You may remember that he turned up in the film *Carmen Jones* as a heavyweight boxer called "Husky Miller"!)

And the man's posture, as you can see, is absolutely ideal for a tired bullfighter, or indeed for a horizontal heavyweight. The lady's role is therefore the active one in the Seville position.

But all she really has to do is to stand by the side of the bed, hitch up her skirt (if she's wearing one), and then sit down upon her *señor*'s erect *órgano* – guiding it lovingly into her *abertura*.

And if you've read this much of the book, you hardly need me to tell you that the aforesaid agreeable little *abertura* must first be thoroughly *lubricada*. It would indeed be *loco* to undertake this exotic position without first ensuring that the lady's love-honey is flowing freely. As a noted Spanish textbook on sex has it:

> "*Sin el juego-amoroso, la vagina estaria*
> (Without the love-play, the vagina will be
> *tan seca que la relación sexual resultaria*
> so dry that the sexual relation will be
> *muy desagradable para la mujer*
> very disagreeable for the female

(y no muy divertidå para el hombre)."
(and not much fun for the bloke either).)

Once the fair lady has impaled herself (so to speak) on her gent, all she has to do is to bounce up and down on him. If necessary, she can take some of the weight on her feet.

He, lazy fellow, need do nothing but lie back and enjoy himself. It is certainly possible for him to lovingly stroke her clitoris (if he doesn't mind split infinitives), but he may well find it easier to peel an orange, or toy with her castanets.

FOOTNOTE: inquisitive readers are doubtless wondering why I have insisted that the gent on the bed should not be called a "toreador". It's because there's no such word in Spanish; it was just made up for the opera. (Honest: look in any Spanish dictionary.)

POSITION NUMBER FOURTEEN: CLITORIS RATING: C C C

The Grenoble (or Lean-back)

Some say that this week's position is named after the pleasant town of Grenoble in the French Alps – where you have to lie pretty far back to get a view of the mountain tops.

Be that as it may, this is quite a sensual position, and one that I'd strongly recommend for couples who've successfully got through the first three months or so of our course!

I know it looks quite difficult to get into, but it's dead easy, really. You, *madame*, begin by kneeling astride your bloke – with one knee on either side of him. Your knees should be at about the level of his hips, so that (not to put too fine a point on it) his erect penis is just underneath your vulva.

When you're ready, put him inside. Next comes the vital manoeuvre of the Grenoble position: *you lean very slowly backwards*. Carry on until your head is on the bed, somewhere in the general region of his feet. WARNING: YOU *MUST* HOLD ON TO HIS WRISTS AS YOU LEAN BACK.

Incidentally, if your knees are at all stiff or rheumaticky (or if your back is not as supple as it used to be), you may find it very difficult to perform this "lean-back". So what you do in these circumstances is to begin in a *sitting* (rather than a kneeling) position, astride your chap – with your legs straight out in front of you.

Either way, you should now be in this well and truly "laid

back" position. I'm afraid that conversation with your guy won't be too easy from now on – unless, of course, you ring him up on your portable phone!

But you, ma'am, will find the sensations which you experience quite entertaining, especially because of the fact that his erect organ will be pressing up against your "G-spot".

And the Grenoble position does have the added advantage that it gives your man very easy access to your clitoris with his hand; indeed, it's one of the few love-making postures in which *he can actually see it*! Furthermore, if you get him to move his fingers upwards and press on the lowest part of your tummy – just above your "pubes" – you'll find that you have a tingly feeling which has been described as "uniquely enjoyable".

Can I just finish by explaining that this "contortionist-type" position *isn't* the sort of one in which the average bloke could easily climax (though his lady might!). So the idea is that you just try it out for a few minutes – as a *divertissement* along the way – before finishing off in some more comfortable posture, in which it's easier for the man to blast his way to orgasm.

POSITION NUMBER FIFTEEN:
CLITORIS RATING: NIL

La Volta

Position invented by Alessandro Volta (1745–1827), the great Italian physicist, who developed the first apparatus – called the "electrophorus" – which generated static electricity by induction.

Or at least, that's what the physics textbooks say. But recent research indicates that instead of using induction, he actually generated the electricity by seduction . . .

Yes, searching for a way of generating a decent voltage, he hit on the idea of persuading his mistress, the lovely Gina Batteria-Vibratore, to come into the laboratory with him and make love.

Naturally, he wired them both up to the dials of his electrical apparatus before they started – and the rest is history.

Now I expect you'd like a sensible description of the position at this point, wouldn't you? Very well.

It's a "female-superior" posture (for that reason, not often used in Italy, I may add). In fact, in a way it's very like the Missionary position turned upside down.

Some people don't like these "lady on top" positions, because they feel having the man underneath is somehow "demeaning" to his virility. Personally, I reckon that's a load of old rubbish!

(In fact, this position is generally considered by sex experts

33

to be particularly *good* for men. Sex therapists of the Masters-Johnson persuasion actually prescribe it for blokes who are having a little trouble with their erections. This is partly because the position is a fairly exciting one, and partly because it makes entry so much easier. When a chap makes love in a male-superior position, it's awfully easy for his erection to collapse just as he's trying to enter.)

Please note that for really adequate and fulfilling penetration, the woman's legs must be OUTSIDE the man's, as in our picture. This feature distinguishes La Volta from other woman-above postures, such as the famous "Mother Superior", which produces quite different sensations for both the lady and the gent.

The Clitoris Rating for La Volta is – as with most other face-to-face positions – absolutely awful, since basically he can't reach it. But he certainly ought to be able to produce quite an electric tingle in her bottom.

P.S. Yes, Alessandro Volta *did* exist. And yes, the volt *is* called after him. If your son is taking GCSE Physics, just ask him. (But don't mention the mistress . . .)

POSITION NUMBER SIXTEEN: CLITORIS RATING: C

The Tivoli

Old Danish position, much used in the famed Tivoli Gardens of Copenhagen – possibly by ladies who charge a little Danegeld for demonstrating it.

Many people know that the Tivoli is a beautiful and romantic spot; few know that it spells "ILOVIT" backwards. Curious, that.

Well, p'raps the young lady in our picture is saying "I love it backwards" as she enjoys her tasty Danish pastry. Who knows?

Enough jokes. This is a very good position for pregnant women, who can enjoy it to the full without having any weight put on their tummies.

It's also excellent for the many ladies who have arthritis of the hip, and who can therefore no longer make love in the regular way without pain. (I get quite a few letters from over-fifty couples who have that problem.)

I'd also recommend the "Tivoli" for any woman who's recently had an abdominal operation; few wives are very enthusiastic about having the weight of a fourteen-stone husband resting on their scar!

And what about all the rest of us? Well, for pretty well *anybody* the "Tivoli" is a nice comfortable position. It lets the husband get far up inside when he reaches his climax, and it produces lots of pleasant (if slightly bumpy) feelings for the wife. Its only major defect is that he's miles away from her clitoris – and breasts.

To get into the Tivoli position, proceed as follows. The lady should lie *on her side* on the bed, and bend right forward so that the top half of her body is at a right-angle to the bottom half. She then raises her thigh just a little, in preparation for accommodating her man.

He needs to lie on his side, immediately behind her, but he remains upright. He gently inserts his *membrum virile* (this is a posh Latin expression meaning "cock") between her thighs, and slides it up inside her. And away they go.

If you want to make the sensation of climax even more pleasingly languorous, then try one or both of these variations:

1. Hamlet (or whatever this blooming Dane is called) leans *right back*, and even further away from the lady, so that the pressure of the back of her vagina pushes his penis downwards at a very considerable angle.

2. Turning to country matters, the fair Ophelia can greatly increase her personal pleasure by thrusting one of her legs *back between his thighs*, so that her heel comes up between his buttocks. I'm told that the feeling induced by this sudden tilt of her pelvis is quite exquisite. Mmm – mmm!

POSITION NUMBER SEVENTEEN: CLITORIS RATING: C

The Athens

I'd just like to reassure you that the couple in the picture are most definitely NOT getting up to anything indelicate involving the young lady's bottom.

You won't find anything like *that* in this book – not least because "bottom intercourse" remains illegal in England – even between husband and wife! Furthermore, I must stress that if you're not careful, it can be a rather unhygienic business. Nevertheless, various British and American surveys suggest that a high proportion of married couples have tried it: thirty-nine per cent in my own national sex survey.

Now "bottom sex" has always been (rightly or wrongly) associated with Greece – at least, in the eyes of other Europeans. It's no coincidence that a well-known French method of saying "go away" is *"Va t'enculer chez les grecques"* – which means "Kindly go and b****r yourself with the Greeks".

However, I'm reliably informed that the Greek god and goddess in the picture are practising absolutely straight and wholesome *vaginal* sex in the Athens position. Furthermore, they're married. To each other. So that's OK.

If (like these two Greeks bearing gifts) you'd like to try the old Athenian position, here's what you do.

After a little spicy foreplay – or, as the Greeks call it, *taramasalata* – the goddess should adopt a standing position,

and then bend over so that her upper trunk is horizontal.

The god now approaches her from behind, keeping a careful eye on his target. Really *skilled* inhabitants of Parnassus could actually enter that target without any manual help: hence the "look no hands" gesture of the young Apollo in our picture.

Nonetheless, us mere mortals should take considerable care when entering from the rear, so as not to cause our partners any discomfort. A careless entry at the angle shown could very easily be uncomfortable, specially for a lady who has not had any children.

Once in, take it at a gentle pace, and achieve your mutual Olympus in your own time.

NOTE: the woman doesn't *have* to stand with her arms stretched out as shown! Indeed, it may be better to rest her hands on some convenient piece of bedroom furniture. But best make it something sturdy, since otherwise it may well get knocked over during the final surges of passion. Whoops!

POSITION NUMBER EIGHTEEN:
CLITORIS RATING: C

The Béziers

After the hurly-burly of last week, here's a nice, gentle, romantic position: the "Béziers". It's called after the town of Béziers in the Languedoc, famous for its brass bedsteads and its pussies. The brass bedstead will play a prominent part in what follows . . .

Now at first sight, the "Béziers" may look very like the Missionary position (which we did in Week Three, remember? I *do* hope you've been paying attention!).

But the fact is that in the study of sexual positions, experts have found that moving your limbs just a matter of a foot or two, or changing the angle of a knee or hip, is enough to completely alter the sensations which you and your partner experience.

So, in the Béziers position the lady (in particular) will find that she senses quite different "vibrations" from those which she feels in the "Missionary" one.

Indeed, some women find that they can't achieve orgasm at all in the "Missionary" – *but they can in this position*. That seems to be because these ladies need to have their legs STRAIGHT in order to be able to "come".

And in fact, that's the main difference between the two postures. In the "Béziers" method of making love, the woman's legs are dead straight. More than that, she should have the soles of her feet pressed hard against the bedposts, so that her thighs are spread very wide. She should use the bedposts as a sort of "platform" to spring from as she meets her man's thrusts. As a variation, she can hook her feet round the bedposts – and pull herself downwards.

As to him? Well, he simply has to lie between her wide-parted thighs and have a wonderful, romantic time, pausing only occasionally to sip a glass of Roussillon and stroke the pussy.

Which reminds me: "Béziers" does have the advantage over the "Missionary" of giving slightly better access to the lady's clitoris – simply because her thighs are spread so wide. The chief *disadvantage* of the position is this: if *madame*'s vagina has become a little lax (in a muscular, rather than a moral sense, I hasten to add) because of being a Mum, then spreading the thighs wide may make things worse. In these circumstances, it may be better to switch to a "thighs together" position, such as "Paris University Club" (see Week Twenty-Three).

POSITION NUMBER NINETEEN: CLITORIS RATING: NIL

The Brive

In Britain, this is often known as the "Frog" position – not because of its French origins, but because of the fact that the agreeable movements of the knees which the lovers make during intercourse are rather like those of a frog swimming.

But in France, this amusing little posture is traditionally associated with the town of Brive-la-Gaillarde, in the *département* of Corrèze, where it's a regular feature of the annual Music Festival.

(By the by, you don't have to do it on a piano, but it certainly adds a certain *je ne sais quoi* to the whole thing if you do. Make sure it's a grand one.)

So what the good citizens of Brive do when they want to make love is this. *Monsieur* lies flat on his back, and spreads his legs very wide. *Madame* – or even possibly *mademoiselle*, I'm afraid – embraces him, placing the soles of her feet (and this is the vital point) on the top surfaces of *monsieur*'s turned-out feet.

In fact, BOTH pairs of feet must be fully turned outward, rather like froggies' tootsies. This simple trick will bring the inner surfaces of both pairs of thighs firmly together in the most intimate and passionate way . . .

Try this manoeuvre, and you will immediately find that it produces quite outrageous and abandoned sensations!

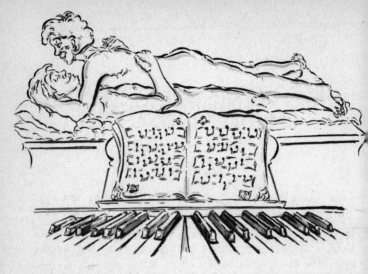

And what the pair of you do next is simply to bend and straighten your knees repeatedly, like a frog easing his way across a pond. *Magnifique!*

Incidentally, few people know that this was the position used by Trevor Howard and Celia Johnson in the film *Brive Encounter*.

FOOTNOTE: for a variation, ladies, try just putting ONE foot on your husband's instep while letting the other one do something else (like tinkling a few notes on the piano). This is known as the Semi-Brive position.

POSITION NUMBER TWENTY:
CLITORIS RATING: NIL

The Racing Club

Now if both of you are fit and healthy and athletic, here's just the position for you. But please *don't* try it if you've got a bad back; you could end up in Position Number 453, the Spinal Traction.

Also, do please bear in mind another possible hazard of the Racing Club posture. If the lady falls off the gent in mid-ecstasy (so to speak), she could cause him a fracture in a very painful place. So do read my instructions very carefully.

Anyway, this position is called after the great Parisian sports club, "Le Racing". (If you don't believe there's such an organisation, read my footnote.)

From its earliest days, the club has produced wonderful athletes in sixteen different sports. Even today, the French national Rugby side contains the great name of Jean-Baptiste Lafond plus three of his Racing Club colleagues.

I'm told that in the 1920s, the club's Rugby team was so gloriously eccentric that its three-quarters turned out wearing berets! And for all I know, they may well have had a Gauloise dangling from the lower lip, and a *sac* of garlic up the jockstrap.

Well now, the Racing Club position started like this. You know how certain British sportsmen insist on leaping on each other, and hugging and kissing in a jolly unmanly way? The lads of the Racing Club were rightly contemptuous of this soppy behaviour; so when *they* scored, their reaction was quite different.

The scorer simply dashed across to the touchline and – with typical Gallic flair – embraced some excited young lady supporter. Before long, it became the custom for the beautiful female fan to greet the try-scorer with open arms – and indeed to jump straight into the position shown here.

However, I certainly wouldn't advise *you* to jump into it, dear lady reader, for the reasons I've already indicated! A more sensible approach is to stand in front of your man, giving him a big, loving hug. When you're ready, gently pop him inside you. Finally, putting your weight on his shoulders as shown, swing your feet forwards and upwards and lock your legs round his waist. (Incidentally, do WARN him beforehand, won't you?)

Finally, the pair of you just rock happily to and fro for as long as his legs can stand it. In practice, most couples have to switch to some less strenuous posture before going for *l'orgasme*.

FOOTNOTE: everything I have said about the sporting achievements and *panache* of the Racing Club is true. I refer you to an article in *The Independent* of 13 March 1991 which reveals that Le Racing's Rugby side have recently turned out in pink bow-ties and knickers, plus gold boots. They still won.

POSITION NUMBER TWENTY-ONE: CLITORIS RATING: C C C

The Nero

Legend has it that as Rome burned, the Emperor Nero was fiddling. But fiddling with *what*?

Well, it wasn't with a violin, that's for certain – because the instrument hadn't been invented! (The one on the pillar over on the left is a wholly understandable anachronism.)

No: the truth is that Nero had been trained in love-play (and, in particular, in the art of caressing the loved one's clitoris) from an early age. His governess gratefully described him as "a prodigy fiddler" – or, according to some historians, "a frodigy piddler".

Naturally, he specialised in positions which gave him a chance to exercise his unusual digital dexterity in order to make his partner happy.

And it was this particular position that he and his wife Poppaea Sabina were engaging in when Rome went up in flames.

I don't think it was their mutual orgasm which actually *caused* the conflagration, but certainly our picture lends new meaning to the expression "Do you smoke after sex?"

Being serious for a moment, the Nero position – like most rear-entry ones – does give the chap an excellent chance to stimulate his lady's *pudenda* with one hand and (if she so wishes) her breasts with the other one.

Poppaea's leg position, you'll notice, is very different from the leg positions in other rear-entry postures, and this fact helps to give the lady some truly *outré* sensations as her man thrusts very deeply within her. I think you'll enjoy it.

So well done, Nero: a man who, whatever his appalling personal defects may have been, was at least an expert in the *ars amatoria*.

As he himself said, shortly after the events recorded in our picture:

O qualis artifex pereo!
(Ah – what an artist dies with me!)

POSITION NUMBER TWENTY-TWO: CLITORIS RATING: NIL

The Pull-On

A very raunchy position this week, dear readers. Don't attempt it unless you are feeling amorous and energetic – for it's both vigorous and exhausting!

What you do is this. The guy lies flat on his back, either on a bed or any other firm surface. His lady – who must of course be thoroughly well prepared and well lubricated and well romanced – kneels astride him, facing *away* from him.

As with most of these rear-entry positions, it'll probably be better if she puts him inside, rather than just having him lunge around hopefully. (Oops!)

She may first have to stimulate him a little by hand, in order to bring him to full erection. (Indeed, this position is particularly good for a man whose erection can sometimes be a bit shaky – because it does enable the wife to *help* the husband to get erect. Furthermore, the fact that SHE is responsible for "entry", rather than him, does take quite a lot of psychological pressure off the poor man.)

Now he's inside her, what happens next? Well, he grasps his lady's loins – that is, the upper part of her hips – and pulls her firmly downwards with his two hands. The effect of this is simply to draw the couple very close together indeed; the tip of his penis should now be very deep inside her.

From then on, the man simply pushes the woman upwards

with his hands, and then pulls her downwards again. She may choose to accept all this quite passively to start with. But after a while, she may elect to add to her own enjoyment (and his) by gently moving her bottom forward and backward. Another pleasant idea is for her to *rotate* it in a small circle, while he continues to pull and push.

Orgasm in this position is usually delicious, but the "Pull-On" does have one defect. It's unusual among rear-entry postures, in that the man can't reach his loved one's clitoris – at least, not unless his arm is about five feet long! But he can of course excite her by caressing the curves of her buttocks.

And if the lady needs clitoral stimulation in order to reach orgasm, the solution is easy: she can simply take matters into her own hands.

POSITION NUMBER
TWENTY-THREE:
CLITORIS RATING: C C C

The Paris University Club

Gosh, have I got a nice, romantic position for you this week! So, light a few candles, put on an Edith Piaf CD, crack open a bottle of Safeways' finest Muscadet, and away we go . . .

This, as you can see, is a "chair" position: Paris University Club (PUC) is a pleasant, comfortable posture in which you, ma'am, just sit across the lap of the man you love – while he, seated on a reliable chair, gently has you from underneath.

Both of you may well be able to go right through to orgasm in the PUC position if you want to. A lot of ladies (though not all) find it fairly easy to climax in this posture, partly because of the very easy access which the man's hand has to the clitoral region.

I must add that the PUC is specially useful in pregnancy, because there's bags of room for the expectant Mum's expanding tummy; love-making therefore involves no discomfort at all for her.

There are various "chair" positions, and this one of course is a *sideways* one – in which the woman's thighs are at right angles to the man's. But if she wishes, she can actually swivel round while doing "Le PUC" – so that she first faces away from him, and then ends up facing across his thighs, but in the opposite direction from the one in which she started. (I'm sure that's quite clear, isn't it? Just hold the book in one hand, madam, and you can't go wrong.)

"PUC", as you'll have gathered, stands for "Paris University Club". This is the famous existentialist nightclub, situated on the left bank of the Seine (naturally) and much favoured by students at the Sorbonne.

At one time, young couples who had nowhere else to go for privacy would resort to making love at this discreet nighterie by using the PUC position.

You can see why. As long as the girl was wearing a voluminous skirt, the fact that the young lovers were actually having intercourse could not be detected by the *gendarmes*, or even by the undercover agents of the dreaded CRS (*Compagnie pour la Répression de la Sexualité*).

You too may perhaps find it exciting and romantic to make love in this position "under the skirt". But please do confine such antics to your own dining-room; they won't go down a bomb at the Nag's Head . . .

POSITION NUMBER TWENTY-FOUR: CLITORIS RATING: C C C

The Basic Flanquette

Well, it's Week 24 and you're getting to be pretty advanced students of Kamasutrology by now, so it's time to introduce you to a major new series of positions: the flanquette group. (Pronounced "flonkette".)

The flanquettes are the ones in which the chap puts one of his legs through the lady's legs FROM IN FRONT. There's a totally different series of positions in which he puts his leg between hers *from the back*, but we'll get to those later, if you can stay the course.

Now, sir, you may be surprised at this, but the simple expedient of thrusting your leg between your partner's thighs creates not only a whole new group of positions, but also a whole new group of sensations for both of you.

Here we show what I call the "basic" flanquette technique – but once you've grasped the principle of pushing the gent's thigh between the woman's fair *cuisses*, you can move on to all sorts of variations which you could more or less work out for yourself.

Anyway, in order to try out the "Basic Flanquette", here's what you do. The two of you should lie on your sides on the bed, couch, chaise-longue or whatever. In fact, our illustration shows a couple on a banquette – having a bonkette in the

flanquette, so to speak! As you see, they're facing each other.

Now the man gently pushes his *uppermost* leg between her thighs – ideally, so that his own thigh is pressing up between the two cheeks of her bottom.

She now takes him in her hand and – after a certain amount of pleasant dallying which might, for instance, involve her in rubbing the tip of his organ against her clitoris – she puts him inside. That's all there is to it; you can go all the way to climax if you wish.

The flanquette position is jolly nice for the chap, I can tell you – but not just for him! Independent-minded women (f'rinstance, ladies who read *The Independent*) tend to like it a lot, because it gives them a good deal of manual control of what's going on.

In particular, if the woman reaches down and puts one hand firmly on her man's buttock, she can actually control (i) the depth to which he thrusts; (ii) his speed; (iii) his rhythm; and (iv) his angle of penetration.

If you fancy yourself as a "New Man", it can be very agreeable to be "used" for the lady's pleasure in this way.

POSITION NUMBER TWENTY-FIVE:
CLITORIS RATING: C C C

The Avignon

Sur le pont d'Avignon,
On the bridge at Avignon,

On y danse, On y danse.
There one dances, there one dances.

Sur le pont d'Avignon,
On the bridge at Avignon,

On y danse, tous en rond.
There one dances, all in a ring.

Les beaux messieurs font comme ça;
The handsome gents do like that;

Les belles dames font comme ça;
The pretty ladies do like that;

Sur le pont d'Avignon, on y danse tous en round.
etc., etc., etc.

If like me, you sang that traditional French ditty as a youngster, you may well have wondered wot on earth the *beaux messieurs* and the *belles dames* were doing.

Well, they may have been doing *this*, I suppose. Certainly, the Avignon position is an immensely pleasurable one, and (I'm glad to say) a very romantic one too. One authority on sexology actually rates it at seventy-five per cent on the romance scale.

Please be warned that penetration can be very deep in the Avignon position. That's fine for experienced lovers who have long grown used to each other's bodies. For a young lass, starting out on the road of love, it may all be a bit too much!

However, assuming that you're a couple who know and love each other well, and who feel totally comfortable with each other in bed, then this is what you do . . .

You, *madame*, lie back on the bed, preferably with a couple of nice, fluffy pillows under your head – or, even better, under your bottom.

You, *monsieur*, kneel down between your lady's thighs as shown in our picture, supporting her knees at about the level of your elbows. You'll notice that one of the joys of this position is that it gives you superb access to your lady-love's clitoris, pubic hair, and other domains that there adjacent lie . . .

And what do you do then? You just enter *madame*'s coral chamber, and . . . well . . . do *comme ça*. If you like, you can sing along to the tune of the famous song as you do it – you'll find the rhythm fits rather well . . .

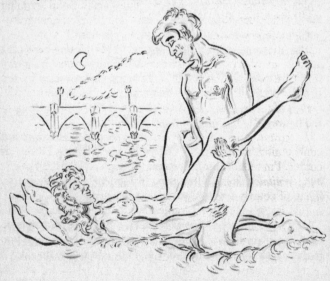

POSITION NUMBER TWENTY-SIX:
CLITORIS RATING: C C C

The Sixty-Nine

At my advice columns, I frequently get letters from couples who're confused about what the 69 position is. Lots of people actually think that the title "69" (or *soixante-neuf*) is the NUMBER of an intercourse position.

Indeed, there's quite a widespread belief that there are ONLY sixty-nine ways of making love: for instance, see the penultimate page of Ian Fleming's *From Russia With Love*, in which the Paris detective Mathis finds James Bond trapping the snarling villainess with a chair – and promptly congratulates him on inventing "the seventieth position"!

But these ideas are quite wrong. The *soixante-neuf* isn't actually an intercourse position at all, as you can see: it's a very sexy love-play technique. It was named *soixante-neuf* by the French because of the fact that when you look down at the bodies of the couple, they do look a bit like a Gallic version of the figures "69". (Well, with the eye of faith . . .)

Le soixante-neuf is arguably France's second most important contribution to European culture – after Sacha Distel, of course. I'm reliably informed that this typically Parisian *caresse bucco-génitale* was much favoured by Queen Marie Antoinette. That, of course, was before she lost her head.

As I say, it's a love-play, rather than an intercourse, position. I'd describe it as a *jeu d'ésprit* in which the couple lie alongside each other on the bed – but with their bodies *reversed*, as you can see, so that the man can lovingly stimulate the lady's genitalia with his lips and tongue, while she does the same for him.

There's another version of the "69" with one partner *under* the other, but some women feel quite threatened by being "submerged" under a man like that. I feel the method shown in our picture is preferable.

So how do you do it? Well, firstly, you need a nice, warm room, so that you're not encumbered by any bedclothes! Trying to do a "69" in chilly old Scotland or England with your head buried under a duvet is a pretty suffocating experience. (Admittedly, a friend of mine once claimed that he could achieve it by using a snorkel.)

If you're not used to this kind of thing – i.e. oral sex – I'd recommend that before actually getting into the "69", you relax each other with some loving and romantic preliminary love-play. (Having somebody's teeth flashing round your genitals all of a sudden can be VERY unsettling.)

Then, when you're both ready, one of you can swing your body round into the *soixante-neuf*, and begin gently nuzzling your loved one's "pubes".

It may well be that, in your early years together, neither of you will want to go all the way to orgasm in this position. Perhaps eventually – who knows?

NOTE: in order to avoid embarrassing social gaffes, always remove your chewing gum before attempting the *soixante-neuf*.

POSITION NUMBER TWENTY-SEVEN: CLITORIS RATING: C

The Bordeaux

Like the "69", the "Bordeaux" is definitely a *summer* position – because really you both need to be fully exposed. It's the sort of thing that's great for making love in a sun-drenched vineyard on the banks of the Garonne or the Gironde. On the other hand, it wouldn't be too good on a parky Friday night in Manchester.

Instructions. Assuming that the lady is athletic (and if she isn't, then don't attempt the position at all), what you do is this. She lies flat on her back and then raises her legs in the air until her thighs are pressing against her tummy. N.B. For obvious reasons, this is not a good poistion to use in pregnancy.

Next, the man smoothly and lovingly enters her, lowering himself forward till his chest is resting on the backs of her thighs. As you can see, this means that her feet are over his shoulders. And from then on . . . well, as they say in Bordeaux, it's *vogue la galère* (full steam ahead)!

An alternative way to get into the Bordeaux position is to start by making love in the "Missionary" (see Week Three). The gentleman missionary then takes hold of the lady missionary's feet and *slowly* raises them till they're over his shoulders.

Penetration in the Bordeaux position is very deep and very satisfying – though some couples may well find it all a bit much,

and might prefer to stay in it for only a minute or two before moving on to something less physically demanding.

Note that it generally helps your enjoyment of this position if you have a bottle of red Bordeaux (i.e. claret) and a couple of glasses at the bedside as you make love.

You may also be interested to hear that there are *variations* of the Bordeaux position, associated with the different types of Bordeaux wine:

In the *Médoc* variation, the lady puts only the RIGHT ankle over the gent's shoulder;

In the *Sauternes* variation, she sweetly crosses her ankles behind his neck;

In the *Graves* variation, he tickles her throughout – and she has to try to maintain her position without laughing;

In the *Entre-Deux-Mers* variation, their two mothers stand on either side of the bed, and look disapproving. (I would not recommend this one.)

POSITION NUMBER
TWENTY-EIGHT:
CLITORIS RATING: C C C

Hector's Horse

I've been completely unable to discover why this well-known position is called "Hector's Horse", though one of the standard American reference books on sexology *The Complete Book of Sexual Love* by Holroyd & Holroyd (published by J. G. Ferguson Inc. of Chicago) says confidently that the ancient Greeks gave it this name.

It's possible: as you doubtless know, Hector was one of the great heroes of classical times ("Some talk of Alexander, and some of Hercules; of Hector and Lysander, and such great names as these . . .").

Despite the fact that nowadays people use his name as a verb – "to hector" – meaning to browbeat or bully, he was probably the noblest and most generous of all the leaders involved in the Trojan War. He dearly loved his wife Andromache and, just as a whimsy, we've pictured him here with her, in the position that bears his name.

Or rather, his horse's name! Zeus alone knows what the horse had to do with it. I can't even claim that the outline of the couple making love (in the foreground) looks anything like the shape of the horse (in the background). Sorry about that.

Nevertheless, the "Horse of Hector" is a good position, and well worth a try. Many couples find it both romantic and sensuous. One woman who tried it out for the first time reported afterwards that it helped her a lot, because it gave wonderful access to her clitoris (for both her and her man).

To get into this position, ma'am, put your personal Greek hero flat on his back, then straddle him with your thighs and put him inside you when you're ready.

Now get him to draw his knees up till his feet are flat on the bed; this means you are resting back against the tops of his thighs. From then on, you can control quite a lot of what's going on by thrusting with your buttocks – so this is a position in which the lady is pretty much in command.

The above-mentioned US sex textbook adds that if the woman "raises herself almost clear of the man's erect phallus, he or she can manipulate it so that the glans is rubbed vigorously against her labia and clitoris, and in the vaginal vestibule." Whew!

DISCLAIMER: This intricate sexual position has no connection with the popular TV programme called Hector's House (or Horse). Honestly.

POSITION NUMBER TWENTY-NINE: CLITORIS RATING: C C

The Benidorm

I once had a letter from a patient who asked for a prescription for "some more of those Benidorm tablets, doctor".

It turned out that what he actually *meant* was the widely used sleeping pill called "Welldorm" – but you can understand the etymological reasons for his confusion!

And after all, Benidorm is a name which has burned itself into the British national consciousness over the last forty years or so. Back in the 1950s it was a tranquil little Spanish village sheltering but a couple of thousand souls. Nowadays it's curiously like a suburb of Clacton – except that more of the waiters are Spanish. Hundreds of Brits spend their holidays there – and vast numbers of them engage in romantic liaisons, with results ranging from the gorgeous to the ghastly.

I like to think that the position we see here was given the name by a couple who had a particularly happy and tender liaison in Benidorm – following which, the boy and girl got married and lived happily ever after, probably in Great Yarmouth. Doubtless they subsequently took their children on holiday to Benidorm each year.

Anyway, if you want to follow this young couple's example, all you do is this.

When the lady is ready for entry, she should kneel on the

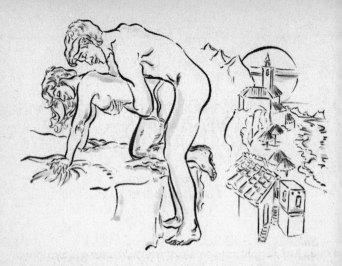

bed, with her knees at the very edge, and her weight resting on her hands.

Her guy now approaches her from behind, and stands close by the bed with his knees outside her calves.

He can now guide himself in – but he must take great care in doing so, because the angle of approach in this position is a rather awkward one. He may not succeed at the first attempt, particularly if the woman hasn't had children, or is rather unused to sex. (It may well be helpful to use a gentle lubricant, such as Johnson's KY-Jelly.)

Finally, he takes hold of her hips, and begins gently thrusting, from time to time using his hands to stimulate whichever areas of her body she wants caressed. Lovely!

NOTE: I know that many readers don't find these "rear-entry" positions very romantic. Yet curiously enough, in one of my recent national sex surveys, it was *romantically minded* ladies who most favoured this type of position. Extraordinary thing human nature, isn't it?

POSITION NUMBER THIRTY:
CLITORIS RATING: C

The Granada

Sultana! I'm living under your spell:
And when you bend over, you feel like a peeled Muscatel.

Actually, I've just been with my wife to the fabulous city of Granada (no, I *don't* mean Manchester), where we heard about this exotic oriental posture.

Granada is quite, quite lovely: I'd strongly recommend any romantically minded couple to find the time (and the money) to spend a night at the wonderful *parador* (inn) which is set in the middle of the Alhambra fortress.

In fact, it was in the pages of Washington Irvine's famous book *Tales of the Alhambra* that we found the inspiration for this position.

As you may know, Granada was in the hands of the Moors for many centuries. The Sultan and his court led a lazy, dreamy, hedonistic life there, thinking of little other than beauty and pleasure.

One particular Sultan, Muley Abul Hassan had a staggeringly lovely wife who used to wander each day to the section of Granada called the *Generalife*.

Now *Generalife* may look like the name of an insurance company, but it's actually one of the world's most glorious water-gardens.

For once, I'm telling you the absolute truth when I say that the Sultan's fair wife used to meet her secret lover in one small secluded part of the water-garden, which today is known as the Court of the Sultana.

Her noble lover used to stand upright, hidden inside the trunk of a great tree which had been split by lightning. And as for her – well, while pretending to do her morning exercises by the tree, she was in fact making love with him – very much as you see in our drawing.

I need hardly say that one day the Sultan discovered the two of them. He promptly killed them – and furthermore, he then did in the whole of the lover's tribe.

If you decided to try this position. I do hope the outcome will be happier for you! Here's what you do.

The man stands upright, preferably bracing himself against something (it needn't be a tree). The lady stands with her back towards him, and gently "retreats" till her bottom is touching him. Then she eases him into her.

Finally, she bends right over *so that her head is resting on a pile of soft cushions on the floor*. Ideally she stays like that till orgasm has been attained . . .

Keep a sharp eye out for Sultans, won't you?

POSITION NUMBER THIRTY-ONE: CLITORIS RATING: NIL

The Toy Boy

This week it's the Toy Boy position, folks. The very fact that there's a position named after the toy-boy phenomenon indicates just how widespread it has become in recent years, doesn't it?

For the "toy-boy syndrome" was almost unknown in the 1950s, and even in the permissive 60s and 70s.

But since the 1980s, there's been a steadily increasing trend for young, athletic men to be kept by (or even married by) ladies of a certain age.

P'raps this is a good thing. After all, maybe it's better for a young chap to be settled down with a mature lady, rather than out "playing the field" and getting into heaven knows what kind of trouble! I know one family who are absolutely *delighted* that their student son is being happily "kept" by a woman twice his age – a woman who (moreover) is clearly experienced in the arts of love, contraception, and good conversation. What's more, she makes sure that he stays home in the evening and works for his degree!

So, here is the ideal position for toy boys: a manoeuvre developed by a certain Famous Lady of the Silver Screen who has a penchant for taking younger lovers – and even younger husbands – to her bed. In a personal communication to me, she assures me that she worked out this position:

". . . so that I could fully appreciate the sight of a young man's peach-textured body, the soft suppleness of his buttocks, and the sheer poetry of the rippling, grooved muscles of his back and legs."

Well! Steamy stuff indeed. Anyway, getting into the "Toy Boy" is quite simple. You begin by making love in the Missionary position, but the gentleman – young or otherwise – then gently swings his entire body round through 90° so that (as you can see in the illustration), he is lying across the bed, and indeed across his lady-love.

This will give her a number of rather recherché sensations, mainly because gentle pressure is being exerted against the *side* of her vagina rather than the more usual places.

At the same time, she can toy with his buttocks if she wishes. A word of warning: if she goes so far as to carry out the caress known as *postillionage*, she should be aware that there are certain hygiene risks to it. *Postillionage* (meaning touching up your partner's rear end) is engaged in by about forty per cent of women, according to my recent *Delvin Report* survey. But if you do this to your toy boy, ladies, you really MUST wash your hands immediately afterwards – please!

POSITION NUMBER THIRTY-TWO: CLITORIS RATING: ½C

The Toulouse

At first sight, a bit like the standard "Missionary" position, from which it was presumably developed. But in fact, this nice, romantic position produces rather different sensations for both *monsieur* and *madame*.

Furthermore, it gives slightly better access to the lady's clitoris than is the case with the "Missionary" – which, as you know by now, is notorious for giving virtually no access at all. Because the man's legs are spread so wide (*outside* the lady's legs, in fact), he does at least have a small amount of room to slip his hand between the two bodies and caress his lady's *cli-cli*. (N.B. In case you're in any doubt, this is a French colloquialism; it means "clitoris".)

In addition, the Toulouse *posture* is particularly useful for the many married couples who've been disappointed to find that their love-making pleasure has been a bit diminished after the lady *has had children*.

It's a fact of life that childbirth – and especially repeated childbirth – does usually make the vagina a little lax.

Fortunately, the Toulouse position exerts a mild "constriction" on the penis – a constriction which you don't get in the "Missionary". So it's ideal for the lady whose tunnel of love has become just a little too loose. (That's why they call it "Toulouse", I expect . . .)

Getting into the Toulouse position is very simple. After preliminary romancing, the lady lies on her back on the bed, and the gentleman enters her *wtih his legs spread wide outside hers*. If you find the actual entry difficult, sir, then begin in the "Missionary" – and after that shift your legs to a position outside your lady's legs, as shown in the drawing.

Once you're in the "Toulouse" it's easy for the man to carry on this position all the way to orgasm. Many women can "come" in this position too. But its drawback – as with so many face-to-face techniques – is the aforementioned poor access to the lady's clitoris.

However, some couples can get over this problem by concentrating on *grinding* their "pubes" very hard together, so as to compress the clitoris. You, sir, will find that this is quite easy in the Toulouse position: press your pubic bone firmly forward and you should be able to feel your lady's clitoris sort of "squelching" gently under you! This may well help her to orgasm.

Finally, why are the Frenchman's trousers on the floor in our picture? Because they are Toulouse, of course. It's enough to make a cat laugh . . .

POSITION NUMBER THIRTY-THREE: CLITORIS RATING: C C C

The Acrobat

Now this really is what I'd call a *position*! We've drawn two circus performers engaging in it, mainly to underline the fact that it really is a VERY acrobatic technique.

Please DON'T attempt it if you have a bad back, or a double hernia, or anything else that could conceivably be thrown out of kilter by doing something as energetic and demanding as the remarkable feat of athleticism shown here.

However, I promise you that the position *can* be achieved by any couple with reasonable suppleness and sense of balance. And to make it in the "Acrobat" is one of the great summits of achievement for a man and woman who are dedicated to conquering all the heights of sexual positioneering.

How do you get into it? Well, you should kick off by getting into the "Racing Club" position, which you may remember from back in Week Twenty. That's the one in which the lady has her legs round the gent's waist, and is clinging on for dear life to his shoulders.

What you do next is this. Having mutually agreed that you're going to attempt the "Acrobat" (and it'd be lunacy for one of you to attempt it without the other's prior concurrence), you make sure that the man is standing very firmly on his two feet, and is securely balanced. His knees should be slightly bent, to take the strain that is coming.

Now the lady starts leaning right backwards. The man should hang on to her arms and support her while she does this. I must stress (and I'm *very* serious indeed here) that she mustn't go back quickly or in an uncontrolled way. That could damage his spine – or, indeed, his penis.

Eventually, she will finish up with her head on the floor, or preferably on a pile of cushions. The man should support her body with his hands during the rest of the action.

You don't *have* to twiddle a ball on the tip of your finger during the proceedings, but it does lend a certain Thespian insouciance to the whole thing.

Women will find it difficult to actually "come" in the Acrobat position, but I suppose it is possible, especially as this extraordinary posture does offer the gent quite unrivalled access to the lady's *kitzler*.

The man should be able to climax, however. Indeed, I'm told that one of the great Edwardian acrobats actually sired a distinguished son while standing in the attitude shown here. It's for that reason that I have no hesitation in classifying it as a Major position. Oh yes.

POSITION NUMBER THIRTY-FOUR:
CLITORIS RATING: C C C

The Snuggles

Jolly nice, cosy, romantic position this week – and, you must admit, far easier than last week's one.

One of the good things about it is that it's very, very easy for both of you to go all the way to orgasm if you want to.

And the "Snuggles" is particularly helpful for ladies who have a bit of trouble in getting turned on, or in reaching a climax.

Why? Because it's totally non-demanding; you don't have a lot of weight on you; you can control your man's depth of penetration yourself to a very large extent; and both you and he have ample access to your clitoris. Indeed, you could very easily use a vibrator for additional stimulation in the "Snuggles" position if you want to. No wonder it's so popular with the *cliterati* . . .

Anyway, in order to try the "Snuggles", here's what you do.

Choose a warm room in which you'll both be comfortable. Put on some sweet music – and soft lights wouldn't be a bad idea, either. Scatter some nice, comfortable cushions on the floor. Settle yourselves on them, and spend a happy twenty minutes or so in friendly love-play.

When you both feel ready for snuggling, the bloke should sit himself upright. (If he hasn't got an erection at this moment, you, ma'am, should help him to get one.)

Now the lady should gently lower herself on to him, putting him inside, inch by inch, with one hand, while she uses the other to support herself.

Meantime, he should stroke her breasts, and generally support her round the bottom and thighs.

Once you're "as one" (so to speak), then you, ma'am, will be more or less in control from now on. Push your buttocks back into him; wiggle them round in circles; bounce them up and down: the choice is yours. And make sure he gives your clitoris plenty of rubbing and caressing while all this is going on.

Have fun.

POSITION NUMBER THIRTY-FIVE: CLITORIS RATING: C C

The Forth Bridge

They're a gallant, hardy bunch of lads and lasses up in Caledonia Stern and Wild. Anybody who knows the Scottish people will be aware of their enthusiasm for throwing brilliantly engineered bridges across almost anything (but especially across Firths).

Well, this position is an example of just that fine, enterprising Scots spirit. It's clear that at some stage back in the misty history of the Highlands, a loving couple decided that it might be no' a bad wee idea to make a bridge between two pieces of furniture.

As you can see, it's Jock's body that forms the bridge. What he has to do is to lie down flat with his back on a stool (or a bed would do), and his feet supported on a nearby haggis, or other solid, reliable object. (Don't choose anything that's too *high* off the ground; otherwise the position won't work.)

Now that he's "bridging the gap" – so to speak – the next thing is for the couple to make sure that he has an erection. N.B. He should first remove his sporran. Making love in a kilt is actually very nice, comfortable, romantic and (above all) cosy. But having an erection under a sporran is dodgy.

Next comes the moment of truth. Flora MacDonald (or whatever the good lady's name is) steps right across him so that she is "straddling" him. She then gently takes hold of his caber

and, instead of tossing it in the traditional fashion, guides it gently inside her. And awa' they gang . . .

You'll note that we've drawn the lady *facing* the gent. This, of course, gives him excellent access to her clitoris, so there's a pretty good chance that she'll be able to reach orgasm in this position if she wants to.

But in an alternative version of the "Forth Bridge", the woman simply faces AWAY from the man. Clitoral access will be more limited here. I did think of calling this alternative technique the *Tay* Bridge position. But I decided against it, in view of the fact that the Tay Bridge is so strongly associated in the public's mind with the word "disaster". Better not to tempt fate.

POSITION NUMBER THIRTY-SIX:
CLITORIS RATING: C C C

The "X" Position

Yes, this is the real X-Certificate position – definitely for adults only! No under eighteens, please.

Actually, I'm kidding. (Oh – you guessed?) The truth is that I gave it the title of "X-position" when I first invented it, simply because of the fact that the couple's four legs do make a sort of "X" – with the centre of the "X" being the point where their sex organs meet in loving union. At least, I hope it's loving.

It's a very satisfying position, this one, but also a very complex one. So please pay attention, and follow the instructions carefully! To avoid confusion, I've directed them all to the lady partner:

1. Get your bloke to lie on a nice comfortable bed or couch, with some pillows or cushions behind his back.
2. Sit on top of his "naughty bits", facing him, with your legs outstretched.
3. Gently put him inside you.
4. Put your RIGHT leg over his RIGHT shoulder.
5. Then put his RIGHT leg over your LEFT thigh, so that his RIGHT foot finishes up somewhere near your LEFT shoulder, as shown in the drawing. (Phew!)
6. By pulling on his hands, as the woman is doing in our drawing, you can now really "draw" him into you. You can achieve very deep penetration if that's what you like.

Tricky, isn't it?

Indeed, when I first published details of this position in one of my agony columns some years ago, it proved almost impossible to find an artist who could draw it.

So my editor decided to get two live (and naked) models to *pose* the position for a photographer.

Alas, I understand that the photo session soon turned into total confusion as legs and arms got mixed up everywhere.

Eventually, I received a frantic phone call from the photographer, who said: "Doctor, d'you mind coming down to my studio and sorting out this here X-position? The couple keep falling off the bed!"

You have been warned . . .

POSITION NUMBER THIRTY-SEVEN: CLITORIS RATING: C

The Offside

This amusing little tactic is called "Offside" simply because it's one of the "on the side" group of positions. (You've heard of "having a bit on the side"?)

But as you can see, both the man and the woman lean slightly *outwards* as they're making love to each other – hence the description *off*side.

If they have a mirror on the ceiling – and, let's face it, who among soccer's *cognoscenti* DOESN'T have one these days? – this will provide them with quite a stimulating view of their union.

It's not obligatory to dress up like the two fans shown in our picture, whose names are Sid and Doris Bonkers, as I'm sure you've guessed.

But if you're seriously into the noble game of football, then you might possibly enjoy donning your favourite team's colours before the Big Match.

Actually, wearing football socks for love-making isn't as unusual as you'd expect: in one of my recent national sex surveys, we found that no less than sixteen per cent of British males wear socks during sex. (That's one per cent more than the percentage who wear condoms. Honestly.)

To get into this nice, comfortable position:

1. Warm up with a little preliminary love-play.
2. Lie down on the bed, practising man-to-woman marking, as pictured.
3. Gently steer it into the . . . er . . . box.
4. Drive it home.
5. Roll yourselves a bit outwards as shown – rather as if appealing for a penalty from the ground.

And away you go. The point of rolling a trifle outwards, incidentally, is that it alters the angle of insertion of the man's organ. Also, it does give him at least *some* chance to get at the lady's clitoris (which is seldom easy in face-to-face positions), thus giving her a reasonable chance of (a) enjoying herself, and (b) getting a result.

In the true footballing tradition, don't forget to hug and kiss each other a lot afterwards . . .

Latest score: Neasden 0, Masters and Johnson Athletic 1 (Pevsner o.g.).

78

POSITION NUMBER
THIRTY-EIGHT:
CLITORIS RATING: C C C

The Pinner

Some folk do say that this position is named after the delightful
semi-rural Middlesex suburb of Pinner, situated at the con-
fluence of the mighty rivers Pinn and Yalding.

Others – perhaps more robust in their views – hold that it is
called Pinner because what the gent does when he leaps on the
lady is to "pin 'er" to the bed. Ye gods!

Anyway, neither of these theories is correct. The fact is that
the one essential ingredient of the position is this: *the gentleman
must romantically kiss and nuzzle the woman's ear, while whisper-
ing sweet nothings in it.*

Now the Latin for "ear" (or, at least, the bit of it which you
can see) is *"pinna"*. And it is this word which has been
corrupted by sexologists through the centuries, into its present
form of "Pinner".

Now to be just a teeny bit more serious, this is an excellent
and quite romantic position. Some couples aren't too keen on it
to begin with, because they feel that the lack of face-to-face
contact is a little depersonalising. But as I've indicated, you can
keep contact with each other by voice – the man can whisper
into the woman's ear, and (by turning her head slightly) she can
tell him what she wants.

What she wants, in fact, may well be stimulation of her

clitoral area, for which this position is very well suited. It's extremly easy for the man to slip his hand round and caress her to the point of ecstasy.

Interestingly, this position is also popular with ladies who want to stimulate *their own* clitorises during intercourse, but who don't want the man to know they're doing it.

That's quite a common situation, because women frequently think that males will disapprove of the female "lending a hand".

In truth, there's usually no need to fear such disapproval; my recent national sex surveys have shown that a very high proportion of men are actually "turned on" by the idea of a woman stimulating herself while being made love to.

Getting into the Pinner position is easy, particularly if the lady has had children. (With a "nullip", gentlemen, you have to take a little extra care.)

The woman simply lies on the bed face down, with legs wide apart, and lets the man stimulate her *shamelessly* (!) till she's ready for entry. Then away you go, and enjoy yourselves . . .

POSITION NUMBER THIRTY-NINE: CLITORIS RATING: NIL

The New Yorker

The New Yorker position is believed to have been named by Dorothy Parker, who used to say that when she lowered herself into it, it was "like landing on the Empire State Building".

(Dorothy's other great sexual shaft – if you'll pardon the word – was to christen her parrot "Onan", *because he wasted his seed*.)

Achieving the New Yorker position is pretty easy, but for the sake of simplicity, I'll address my instructions to the lady partner.

To begin with, ma'am, pick yourself a nice, warm, comfortable room (it doesn't have to be a Manhattan penthouse).

Arrange your bloke on the floor, lying on his back, with some cushions under him if you wish.

Now use Secret Techniques of Erotic Arousal to induce him to give a passable imitation of a skyscraper. If you don't *know* any Secret Techniques of Erotic Arousal, then consult one of the companion volumes in this quite *excellent* series from Hodder & Stoughton, such as *The Book of Love* or *How to Improve Your Sex Life*.

Once you've got him upright and rarin' to go, just squat down over him as shown in the picture, and lower yourself on to him. You should be bent right forward – at least to begin with – because that will give you some interesting and pleasant experi-

ences as his penis presses back hard against the *rear* wall of your vagina.

Then just bounce your bottom up and down – and enjoy yourself. I can tell you that he'll enjoy himself too.

Two drawbacks in this position: the man can't reach your clitoris, unless he has arms like King Kong. And he'll probably keep "popping out". Just pop him back in again.

That's the New York position: so good, you'll do it twice!

FOOTNOTE: I hope poor Dorothy Parker – who didn't have a very happy life – enjoyed herself in the "NY" position. I like to think that it was in this posture (and doubtless in an elegant suite at the Algonquin Hotel) that she thought up another famous *bon mot*:

> "*Men seldom make passes*
> *At girls with small asses.*"

POSITION NUMBER FORTY:
CLITORIS RATING: C C C

The Lisbon

Invented by Vasco da Gama ("Vasco the Game"), the great Portuguese navigator, while on a visit to the Cape of Good Hope.

This is one of the *cuissade* group of positions – that is, the group in which the husband enters the wife from behind, but with one leg thrust between her thighs. (That contrasts with the *flanquette* group of postures, in which the chap puts his leg between her thighs – but from *in front*. See for instance Position Twenty-four.)

Students of linguistics may like to know that I've searched for the word *cuissade* in many dictionaries – French, Portuguese and otherwise – but have been unable to find it. However, it almost certainly comes from the mediaeval French word *cuisseaux*, meaning thigh. And I'm sure we all feel better for learning *that*, don't we?

Anyway, getting into this particular *cuissade* position is quite complicated, which is why I've left it till so late in your fifty-two-week course! A couple of glasses of *vinho verde* will probably help you to get started. After that, the lady should lie on the bed on her LEFT side, with the gent lying behind her, lying on *his* LEFT side too.

He should now gently enter her; this will mean that they're in the Spoons position (Number Ten).

Next, he should thrust his RIGHT leg between her thighs. She will enjoy this (honestly, ma'am – try it and see).

Following all that, the *senhora* should roll on to her back. At this point, the *senhor* must push his LEFT leg under her bottom, sit up, and shove his LEFT foot in the general direction of the edge of the bed. No wonder they called Vasco da Gama "the navigator"!

Finally, the *senhora* thrusts her RIGHT leg up towards the ceiling, supporting it with both hands. The *senhor* pours them both another glass of *vinho*, and away they go. Note that he has two hands free for what the Portuguese call *jogo amoroso*. Hence the very high clitoris rating of this position.

With ingenuity, the Lisbon can be converted into about fifteen different variations. As Elizabeth Barrett Browning says in *Sonnets From the Portuguese* (1850): "How do I love thee? Let me count the ways. . . ."

POSITION NUMBER FORTY-ONE:
CLITORIS RATING: NIL

The Baigneuse

Redolent as it is of the atmosphere of French Impressionism, this position was invented by Pierre Auguste Renoir and Claude Monet (not together, of course) on the banks of the Seine, *circa* 1870.

You could say that it's just a variation on the Missionary position, which we did way back in January. But you'd be wrong.

For although the sensations which the *husband* feels in this gentle, romantic position aren't all that different from those he felt in the "Missionary", the feelings which his wife experiences aren't the same at all.

She'll feel deeper penetration, and a stretched and languorously pleasurable sensation in her loins, as she flexes her knees and hips, and draws her man sensuously into her.

Achieving the "Baigneuse" is fairly straightforward. You don't actually need to do it in a meadow by a river, but if you want to create the illusion, you could both put on bathing things and pretend that your bed is the bank of the Seine at Argenteuil.

You, *madame*, should put your shoulders on the edge of the bed, so that your head hangs a little over it – ideally with your hair dangling down exotically, like the locks of the girl in the picture.

Then just raise your knees to the point shown – and welcome your man in a tender and loving embrace . . .

Alternatively, you can start in the Missionary position, and then flex your hips and knees so that you get into the "Baigneuse". Either way, it's a good idea to cross your ankles behind your *monsieur*'s back and use your legs to really pull him hard into you.

(N.B. As a schoolboy, I was told in the playground that if a woman does this to a man, it kills him! I am happy to report that this is untrue. How sadly misinformed was "Dooce" Downing of the Lower Fifth.)

That's the "Baigneuse", then. If you DO decide to do it on the banks of a French river as shown in our sketch, please don't fall in the water at the moment of climax. You'd be totally in Seine.

POSITION NUMBER FORTY-TWO:
CLITORIS RATING: C C C

The Pyrenees

Most sexologists will tell you that this position was invented high in the French or Andorran Pyrenees, where shepherds and shepherdesses used it to make love – the great advantage being that the shepherdesses (kneeling upright) could keep an eye on their flocks throughout.

But to those citizens who believe this daft theory, I say *Folies Bergères* (you foolish burghers)!

Quite clearly, the title of this position is a corruption of the traditional English phrase, "A pair o' knees". As long ago as Chaucer's day, this expression was used to denote a position in which the woman is on her two knees, astride the man.

And our drawing is really self-explanatory, isn't it?

The man lies on his back. His lady works at him till he's got a really good erection. Then she places a knee on either side of his waist, and gently lowers herself, taking his organ in her hand and guiding it in.

Sometimes the actual "guiding in" is a wee bit difficult. A useful tip in these circumstances, ma'am, is this: moisten the tip of your man's penis by tenderly sucking it for a moment – after that, you should be able to slide him in with no difficulty at all.

Finally, the lady simply bounces up and down, or rocks from side to side – while the man makes use of this position's excellent "Clitoris Rating" to caress her *cli-cli*.

You might be interested to know (and I'm not kidding) that this position is strongly recommended by the great US sex therapists, Masters and Johnson. They use it in the treatment of impotence – because it's much easier for a man to keep an erection while entering in this position.

It's also used by therapists who treat certain common *female* problems – notably nervousness about putting a man inside. The advantage of the Pyrenees position is that the woman has *absolute control* of how far the man goes in. If she's VERY nervous, she can just put him half an inch in to begin with – perhaps progressing over a period of weeks to one inch, two inches, five inches, and so on.

POSITION NUMBER
FORTY-THREE:
CLITORIS RATING: NIL

The Wheelbarrow

Probably invented by Adam and Eve (or possibly by Capability Brown), this one is just the thing for those with green fingers. It's not the most romantic of positions, I agree – but it'll provide a spot of good fun for athletically minded couples who're also gardening enthusiasts!

Whether you actually do it in your garden or not is up to you, but I certainly wouldn't recommend attempting it on the back lawn if you have the sort of neighbours who peek at you from behind the gazebo.

Also, you really MUSTN'T attempt the "Wheelbarrow" if the man has a bad back; seriously, this position could make his spinal problems very much worse. As a matter of fact, it's possible for the couple to "spare" the bloke's back by doing what's called the "Reverse Wheelbarrow" – in which it's the *lady* who stands upright, while the gent imitates the barrow. But that's an unbelievably exotic posture, and well beyond the scope of this simple textbook . . .

Now to get into *la brouette* (which is Frog for wheelbarrow), proceed as follows.

You, ma'am, should lie flat on your face on the ground, with your legs spread wide apart. Your man should then come and

stand with his feet *between* your thighs. The welly boots shown in our picture are optional.

You, sir, should now bend your knees, and take hold of your lady-love approximately in the region of the groins, as shown. Now lift her up to your waist level, using your knees and *not* your back for the "lift". (N.B. This instruction to use your knees and not your back for lifting is VITAL; as a former member of the Education Committee of the Back Pain Association, I can tell you that I'm not kidding!)

You don't have to do much now, ma'am, except to perform the easy handstand shown in our picture, while your guy sort of eases himself into you. Thenceforward, everything in the garden should be lovely . . .

Main drawback of this position is its fairly disastrous clitoris rating (i.e. NIL). That's due to the fact that – unless the lady is very light indeed – the gentleman really will need *both* hands to support her loins, especially as the moment of climax is reached.

POSITION NUMBER FORTY-FOUR:
CLITORIS RATING: C C

The Pisa

There was a young lady of Pisa
Who met a lubricious old geezer;
When he offered her gold
And riches untold,
She said "Certainly not! I take Visa."

I'm glad to say that the Pisa position has *nothing* whatever to do with the quite disgraceful limerick printed above. In fact, the position is in some ways a celebration of the famous occasion when the young Galileo stood on top of the leaning tower of Pisa, and dropped a small cannonball and a feather at the same moment. This indisputably proved something or other – especially to Galileo's dad, who was sitting at the foot of the tower at the time.

Anyway, the general idea in this *postura* is that the lady imitates the leaning tower of Pisa – and so does the gentleman in his own small way.

Begin, ma'am, in a standing position, with your feet about eighteen inches apart. If you want to hold a feather in one hand and a ball in the other, then it's quite OK by me. (I can imagine what you're going to do with the feather, but I'm not sure what you're going to do with the ball.)

Your bloke now steps forward and stands with his feet

between yours. Showing a fine disregard for the laws of gravity, he enters you from below – aiming to do so at approximately the same angle of tilt as that of the famed campanile of Pisa, of course.

He then steadies your haunches with his hands, as shown in the picture, so that you can lean forward at a very considerable inclination. Meanwhile, he leans straight backwards.

The effect of all this is that his own miniature "Leaning Tower" will be pressing back very hard against the *rear* wall of your vagina. This will give you a sensation which is *molto agreabile*, I assure you! Continue for as long as you like, or until one of you falls over.

P.S. Please waste no time in trying this position out. The 180-foot high tower of Pisa is already over seventeen feet out of true, and the angle of tilt is getting worse every month. The collapse of the Great Italian Erection cannot now be long delayed.

POSITION NUMBER FORTY-FIVE: CLITORIS RATING: C

Mother Superior

This position is so called because it's absolutely ideal for the expectant Mum – as it puts no weight at all upon her tum.

That's a matter of great importance, since many of the regular face-to-face positions (like the "Missionary") are absolutely hopeless in pregnancy, thanks to the fact that so many women can't bear the weight of repeated male thrusting on to what is, after all, an *extremely* full tummy! I'm not surprised that one noted textbook of sexology gives this position its top "PPP" rating – meaning that it's absolutely the best for pregnancy.

However, the "Mother Superior" is also jolly good for any adventurous couple who want to try something different – yet comfortable and romantic.

Getting into it is a doddle, really. The man lies on his back, with his legs spread very wide apart (that's important). He then draws his missus towards him in a loving embrace; she should be face down, and with legs together – which should feel nice and snug when he enters her.

Incidentally, the fact that his legs are so wide apart does give him at least some access for his hand to her clitoris – something that isn't really possible in other, closely related face-to-face positions.

There's an old myth about this position, to the effect that it

"demeans" a man, and somehow takes away his virility, simply because he's underneath. Rubbish!

Just try it for yourself, sir – you'll rapidly find that you feel VERY virile indeed.

But I have to admit that the "Mother Superior" *is* a slightly "lazy" position for us blokes. It is (without doubt) the position which was involved in the notorious case of the young woman hospital doctor who became pregnant by a mystery man.

When she was asked who the father was, she replied that she didn't know – because he was just a chap in a white coat who'd slipped into her room one night in the dark, made love to her, and then departed.

"All I can say," sobbed the poor young housewoman, "is that he was a consultant."

"How do you know?" she was asked.

"Well you see: he made ME do all the work."

94

POSITION NUMBER FORTY-SIX:
CLITORIS RATING: C

The Brighton

Another "rear-entry" position here – and a very nice, romantic one, in which the husband can lean forward and whisper sweet and loving things into his missus's ear.

That is, assuming she IS his missus! I certainly hope so – but Brighton (where this position was invented) has, since Georgian days, held a reputation as a place where couples who aren't actually wed can spend a jovial weekend together, with few questions asked by the local hoteliers.

Anyway, gentlemen: to get into the Brighton position, ask your Brighton Belle to arrange herself artistically on a large pile of cushions (or pillows) to give support to her tummy and breasts. Her legs should be spread very wide, in order to give you the best possible access to her charms . . .

While she is in this tempting attitude, you should spend some time (say, twenty minutes or so) in caressing her agreeably exposed buttocks and inner thighs. If she has a personal vibrator, by all means use it – but don't let the buzzing wake up the people in the next room!

At all costs, do not attempt entry till she is very moist, and completely ready for you. When you're *sure* that she wants you to come in, just drape yourself tastefully across her back in the manner shown in our picture, with your legs fairly close together, between hers.

Because her legs are so wide apart, you may be able to achieve some access to her clitoris, but it won't be easy. And because both of you have your hands so far away, I have to admit that there's no easy way of preventing yourself from "popping out" quite frequently. Still, popping in again is a lot of fun.

However, do be careful when you "attempt re-entry". In this position, it is all too easy to give a lady a slight jab in . . . ah . . . the wrong place. Hence the famous Brighton limerick:

> There was a young lady of Brighton
> Who had an unusually tight 'un.
> When her boyfriend said "Love,
> It fits like a glove,"
> She said "Darling, you're not in the right 'un!"

FOOTNOTE: for wonderful romantic weekends in Brighton (*with* your wife, please) I can thoroughly recommend the marvellous Granville Hotel on the seafront. The Noel Coward room has to be seen to be believed.

POSITION NUMBER FORTY-SEVEN:
CLITORIS RATING: C C C

The Beagles

While I was writing my "Position of the Month" column for a certain famous woman's magazine, I received a number of readers' letters requesting me to dream up a position suitable for a tall man and a fairly short woman. This was the result – though in fact, it works out pretty well for almost *any* couple, even if he's two foot six and she's nine feet three.

The reason why tall gents and short ladies sometimes have trouble making love is this. In most sexual postures, they find that the top of the lady's head is only about halfway up the gentleman's chest!

The Beagles position gets round this difficulty, because (as you can see) the woman's head nearly always finishes up *above* the man's, no matter what the disparity in their heights.

Why is it called the "Beagles" position? Well, perhaps it could be after the town called Bègles in south-western France, where all the men are tall and all the women are short. (And if you believe *that*, after reading all the tall stories in this book, you'll believe anything!)

Alternatively, the position could be called after *bagels* – those traditional Jewish hard-baked rolls (with the agreeably Freudian aperture in the centre), often used as an emergency contraceptive in New York.

Or it could be inspired by something I once saw two amorous

beagles getting up to in a rocking chair (with difficulty).

Believe what you will. In any case, the Beagles position is a very comfortable one, and a nice romantic one too. It's ideal for the man who wants to kiss his lady-love's neck and murmur sweet nothings in her ear. It's particularly useful in pregnancy, when an expectant Mum doesn't want a crushed tum.

To achieve the position, proceed like this:

Take one reasonably well-built chair (it doesn't HAVE to be a rocking chair – but it helps!).

Sit the chap on the chair (in cold climates, a cushion or two would be a good idea).

When you're in an appropriate state of enthusiasm, ma'am, lower yourself on to him gradually – helping him in with your hand.

Tell him to caress your clitoris (this is VERY easy in this position).

Sway your hips rhythmically backwards and forwards, and get him to do the same.

That's about it, really. Rock on!

POSITION NUMBER FORTY-EIGHT: CLITORIS RATING: NIL

The Paris Olympics

This week's rather sporty position – the "Paris Olympics" – is so called because the bloke's posture is *exactly* that adopted by the great American pole-vaulter Lee Barnes when he won the P.V. Gold Medal at the famous "Chariots of Fire" Games of 1924 in Paris, thrusting himself upwards to the magnificent height (for those days) of twelve feet eleven and a half inches (three metres ninety-five centimetres).

Now, ma'am, this position does – quite frankly – allow your chap to get a VERY long way up inside you – though not, I hasten to add, as far as three metres ninety-five centimetres!

In order to achieve this very satisfying posture, just get your man to lie flat on his back, on some convenient *terrain de sport* (such as a large double bed).

Then lie on top of him, putting him neatly inside you when you're ready.

Next, ask him to bring his legs right up off the bed till his feet are together – somewhere above the small of your back, perhaps with his heels tapping agreeably on your bottom.

Now that he has achieved the same attitude as the great Lee Barnes, he will be able to use the power of his legs to pull himself up into you, creating *sentiments* which I hope that both of you will find *très beaux*.

There should also be very good contact between his pubic

bone and yours, so that your clitoris ought to receive really quite nice stimulation throughout. *Vive le sport*!

WARNING: This position, as befits its name, is actually a fairly athletic one for a feller. So your man should definitely *not* attempt it if he has a bad back. Or a broken pole.

POSITION NUMBER FORTY-NINE: CLITORIS RATING: C

The Watteau

Invented by the great Franco-Flemish artist Watteau (1684–1721).

Watteau (pronounced "What-Ho", appropriately enough) loved painting pretty girls in swings. The position named after him is a gloriously dotty one in which a skilled and loving couple can achieve a unique method of romantic union.

But make no mistake, *Le Watteau* isn't easy. And I have to admit that very few lovers would be able to continue in this swinging position all the way to orgasm. Indeed, very few would *want* to!

However, the "Watteau" technique can be a delicious prelude to more orthodox forms of intercourse. It's particularly good fun if the lady gets into the spirit of the thing, and dresses herself in ribbons, bows, frills and furbelows (whatever *they* may be). The gentleman could usefully enter into the idea too, by donning some form of early eighteenth-century garb, p'raps including a strategically placed cod-piece.

Basically, all that happens is this. *Madame*, who must – repeat MUST – be well lubricated (maybe in more senses than one), sits on a comfortable swing and rocks gently to and fro with her thighs apart and legs raised a little.

Monsieur – who must also be . . . er . . . well prepared – stands in front of her and facing her, so that every time she swings forward, the two of them can effect a gentle and delicate entry and exit.

It is VERY important that the woman should limit the oscillations of the swing to a matter of about *twelve inches* (thirty centimetres), to and fro. In Greece, I've seen illustrations of a "swing" position very similar to this one, in which a goddess is swooping forward about FOUR FEET towards a god who is waiting to receive her with an erect phallus! My guess is that he ended up in the Urological Department of the Elysian General Hospital.

So, keep it to very short, gentle swings! Clearly, if you're to make this position a success, you need a bit of practice, a good sense of timing, and an excellent aim. But it can be done – and even if you get it a bit wrong, the "near misses" are very good fun indeed.

POSITION NUMBER FIFTY:
CLITORIS RATING: C C

The Gym Mistress

I dunno why this week's position is known as the "Gym Mistress". One authority thinks that it may have been invented by one of those ladies who advertise in phone booths in Bayswater and Holland Park ("Miss Lash, ex-gym mistress of striking appearance, offers corrective therapy for naughty boys . . .").

Personally, I prefer to believe that the technique was really developed by some kind-hearted lady PE teacher who took pity on some poor bewildered lad and helped him find his self-confidence in the gym one day.

Be that as it may, you don't actually need a gymnastic vaulting horse in order to have a go at the "Gym Mistress". A good, solid kitchen chair will do equally well; so too will *any* strong piece of furniture which you can both straddle.

For the sake of argument, let's assume that you've selected a stout wooden kitchen chair (after all, you're a bit unlikely to have a vaulting horse knocking about the house). You, sir, should sit on it, with your feet wide apart, just outside the legs of the chair.

Now you, ma'am, should take hold of your man's organ, and *hold it up against the lower part of his tummy*. This is quite important, because it helps to prevent you from sitting down hard on it, and doing him quite a mischief.

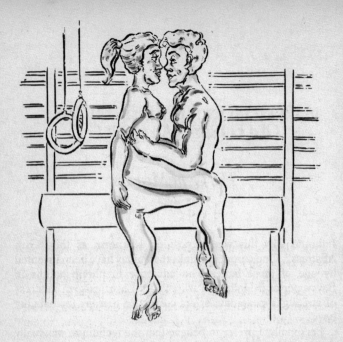

OK – now sit yourself down on his lap, *astride* him and facing him, as in the picture. With your hands, you control his erection – and when you're ready, you put it into you. Super!

Though I've described this position in rather jokey terms, it is actually a very pleasant and romantic one, in which a loving couple can have a very nice time.

For a saucy variation, try doing it with the lady's clothes on – in other words, under the woman's skirt. Obviously, she should remove her pants and her tights first – or just wear open-crotch ones. This all adds to the general sense of "naughtiness" which makes the "Gym Mistress" such fun.

POSITION NUMBER FIFTY-ONE:
CLITORIS RATING: C

The Biarritz

Classy, elegant position, named after the equally classy and elegant resort on France's Southern Atlantic coast.

Women who've tried the Biarritz position speak highly of the fact that it gives the man ample opportunity to pat and caress their bottoms – thereby greatly enhancing the pleasure of love-making and often raising the intensity of orgasm to new heights.

(But if the man uses the *postillionage* caress, he should take care to heed the hygiene warning given in the section on the Toy Boy position.)

The Biarritz is ideal for trying out on a sun-kissed topless or nudist beach, *if* you can find adequate privacy behind a sand-dune. Sadly, I have to report that the main *plage* at Biarritz itself is not suitable for trying out this or any other position. Though it's an extremely erotic place – with vast numbers of topless girls bouncing around with their boyfriends in the rolling Atlantic surf – any attempt at coition would almost certainly attract the attention of the gendarmes.

Nevertheless, let's say you've found your secluded beach somewhere. Simplest way of getting into the "Biarritz" is this. The chap lies down on his back, and the lady lies on top of him. They commence an agreeable spot of intercourse in that position. When they're nice and comfortable, the lady twists herself off to the LEFT, so that her body is now at an angle of about 45° to her man's.

He now thrusts his left leg between hers, as shown, and half sits up so that he can caress her bottom while they make love. (I suppose I should add that this is sometimes known as the "Hot Cross Bum" position.)

If he has a vibrator, this is an ideal opportunity to use it all over her body. But for Heaven's sake don't let the sea water get in it!

POSITION NUMBER FIFTY-TWO:
CLITORIS RATING: NIL

The Chandelier

To celebrate Yuletide and the end of your year's course of study, here's the most exotic position of them all: swinging from the chandelier.

Please do NOT attempt this quite outrageous position unless you have a very strong (and very well-insured) chandelier. At all costs, do not try it if your source of lighting is a 60-watt bulb hanging from a twist of battered flex.

Alas, because of its very nature this method of love-making has until now been confined to the ranks of the aristocracy – and the young, fit ones, at that! But it can be done by YOU, even if your names aren't Lord and Lady Fitznicely.

If you want to have a serious try at it, but do not possess a sturdy chandelier, then proceed as follows.

First of all, the lady must find something firm and dangling to hang from. A simple trick is to make a "rope" out of knotted towels – and attach it securely to your banisters. *I did say "securely" – we don't want any accidents.*

Next, ma'am, get your husband to stand behind you, clasping you firmly round your waist.

Lift one leg slightly, in order to let him enter (after all, it's Christmas!). Then tell him not to let go, at all costs.

Next, take hold of your rope of blankets – or chandelier –

stretching as high above your head as possible, so that you're both on the very tips of your toes.

Finally, just push yourselves off from the ground an inch or two, so that you're swinging free, but *completely* under control at all times. DON'T make wild lurches through space, or you could both end up spending Christmas in Casualty. ("It was like this, doctor . . .")

This position is all very well for the lady who works out a lot at the gym, and who has a fairly light husband! But a lot of women WON'T be able to support their partner's weight easily; in these cases, it's better to do the chandelier position the other way round – in other words, with the man taking the strain.

In order to achieve this, begin making love in a face-to-face standing position. Then let the gent reach upwards for the rope of towels (or whatever), and use his strength to lift the two of you a couple of inches off the ground.

I have never heard of a couple actually reaching a climax in this slightly barmy final position of the year. But if you do happen to make it, I suggest you inform the *Guinness Book of Records*.

AFTERPLAY

Health Warning. If you get stuck in any of our fifty-two positions, don't call me – call an osteopath. In Britain, good osteopaths can be recognised by the fact that they have the letters "DO" and "MRO" after their names.

An alternative would be to call a chiropractor – qualified ones have "DC" after their names.

Whatever you do, don't call your GP – he'll probably shoot me!

Romance Warning. If you've really done one sexual position a week throughout the whole of the year, guided by this book . . . well, you must be dotty! Still, I take off my hat to you. Please write in to me (c/o Hodder & Stoughton), and I'll send you a signed sustificate to say that you've completed the course.

Good luck to you – and may you and your partner go through a lifetime of romance and happy loving together.

DR DAVID DELVIN

IT'S A DOC'S LIFE

Revealing, unusual and frequently hilarious, **It's a Doc's Life** is the life-layed-bare story of one of Britain's best known 'media doctors'.

From his first, fumbling medical student days, to hospital life and then out into the wide and frequently weird, outside world, Dr David Delvin tells all.

TV medic, humorist, 'agony uncle', *Mastermind* contender, failed hang-glider pilot, family planning buff and a member of the highest medical court in the land, he is also the author of a series of bestselling books on sex.

It's a Doc's Life is devastatingly frank and often controversial, mixing farce and tragedy. It will delight and entertain his many readers and viewers.

A Royal Mail service in association with the Book Marketing Council & The Booksellers Association.

Post-A-Book is a Post Office trademark.

DR DAVID DELVIN

THE DELVIN REPORT ON SAFER SEX
(IN THE AIDS ERA)

Once it was the Swinging Sixties.
Now it's the Edgy Eighties – which look like leading us into the Nervous Nineties. Suddenly all the sparkle seems to have gone out of everyone's sex lives and the dangers press in on every side. There's AIDS, herpes, cervical cancer. Hardly a day passes without some new horror story.

So what is to be done?
Of course the stern, traditional moralists are having a field day: muttering about the Wages of Sin and saying, 'I told you so.'

But suppose you're among the millions who *enjoy* sex and want to go on enjoying it?

Safer Sex is for you. Here, clearly set out, are descriptions of what's safe and what's to be avoided, advice on assessing your own risks and how to lessen them. Incorporating the *Delvin Report* on people's sexual habits, recently published in *She* magazine, here is open discussion of everything from monogamy to wife-swapping, from bondage to sex games. Here also are the full medical facts about AIDS and all the other sexually transmitted diseases, about contraception methods and safety precautions.

Safe sex doesn't have to be sex without fun. Imagination is the most important sex aid of all. By charting your own safe path among the real dangers, the scare stories and the Old Wives' Tales, these can still be the Enjoyable Eighties – with the Naughty Nineties to look forward to.

HODDER AND STOUGHTON PAPERBACKS

DR DAVID DELVIN

HOW TO IMPROVE YOUR SEX LIFE

How To Improve Your Sex Life is everybody's guide to making a good thing better, written in straightforward language by a doctor for non-medical people everywhere.

A wide-ranging book that does not moralise but is clear and responsible in its advice and occasional warnings.

A book that does not assume that everyone is some sort of athletic superperson and includes completely up-to-date medical findings and opinions.

But above all a book with one central theme: understanding between men and women. Because improving your own sex life must include improving your partner's. Because sex is something people do *together*, never something one person does *to* another. Every man and woman has worries, needs and failings – as individuals and as couples. All the time emotions and attitudes are stressed as well as techniques.

Packed with facts but not over-solemn in its approach, *How To Improve Your Sex Life* is a helpful, informative, above all encouraging follow-up to Dr Delvin's best-selling *Book of Love*.

HODDER AND STOUGHTON PAPERBACKS

THE DIAGRAM GROUP

QUESTIONS OF SEX

Asking questions about sex is difficult – Who can you ask? . . . Are you embarrassed about asking? . . . Do you know **what** to ask? . . . Can you trust the person you're asking? . . . Do they know the answer? . . . Or will you be fobbed off with a load of rubbish? . . . Will you get a moral lecture instead of a proper answer? . . . Will you **understand** the answer or will it be too technical? . . . Will the right person be there when you really need to know? . . . Will you be laughed at or told not to worry when you're worried sick? . . . Is the person up-to-date enough to know about AIDS or IUDs? . . .

QUESTIONS OF SEX is the solution. Set out in a clear question-and-answer format, it covers the entire range of sexual concerns. The questions have been collected from the files and postbags of doctors, advice columnists, clinics and counsellors. Technical terms are explained, diagrams are used wherever necessary. There is medical and legal advice. Young or old, innocent or think you know it all, male, female, gay, straight, worried or just plain curious . . . **QUESTIONS OF SEX** is a book to turn to any time you need it.

HODDER AND STOUGHTON PAPERBACKS

MORE TITLES AVAILABLE FROM HODDER AND STOUGHTON PAPERBACKS

DR DAVID DELVIN

☐	50252 X	It's a Doc's Life	£3.50
☐	02320 6	The Book of Love	£4.50
☐	41907 X	The Delvin Report on Safer Sex	£2.95
☐	01176 3	Sex Manners for Men	£1.95

DIAGRAM FOR MEN

☐	43078 2	Questions of Sex	£2.50
☐	33101 1	Sex: A User's Manual	£4.50

All these books are available at your local bookshop or newsagent, or can be ordered direct from the publisher. Just tick the titles you want and fill in the form below.

Prices and availability subject to change without notice.

HODDER AND STOUGHTON PAPERBACKS, P.O. Box 11, Falmouth, Cornwall.

Please send cheque or postal order for the value of the book, and add the following for postage and packing:

U.K. – 80p for one book and 20p for each additional book ordered up to a £2.00 maximum.

B.F.P.O. – 80p for the first book, and 20p for each additional book.

OVERSEAS INCLUDING EIRE – £1.50 for the first book, plus £1.00 for the second book, and 30p for each additional book ordered.

OR Please debit this amount from my Access/Visa Card (delete as appropriate).

Card Number   ☐☐☐☐☐☐☐☐☐☐☐☐☐☐☐☐☐

AMOUNT £.......................................

EXPIRY DATE ....

SIGNED ....

NAME ....

ADDRESS ....

....